Audio Technology
Fundamentals

A U D I O   L I B R A R Y

Audio IC Op-Amp Applications, Third Edition
Walter G. Jung

Audio Production Techniques for Video
David Miles Huber

Handbook for Sound Engineers: The New Audio Cyclopedia
Glen Ballou, Editor

Recording Demo Tapes at Home
Bruce Bartlett (John Woram Audio Series)

How to Build Speaker Enclosures
Alexis Badmaieff and Don Davis

Introduction to Professional Recording Techniques
Bruce Bartlett (John Woram Audio Series)

John D. Lenk's Troubleshooting & Repair of Audio Equipment
John D. Lenk

Modern Recording Techniques, Third Edition
David Miles Huber and Robert E. Runstein

Musical Applications of Microprocessors, Second Edition
Hal Chamberlin

Sound System Engineering, Second Edition
Don and Carolyn Davis

Microphone Manual: Design & Application
David Miles Huber

Sound Recording Handbook
John M. Woram (John Woram Audio Series)

Principles of Digital Audio, Second Edition
Ken C. Pohlmann

For the retailer nearest you, or to order directly from the publisher, call 800-428-SAMS. In Indiana, Alaska, and Hawaii call 317-298-5699.

Audio Technology Fundamentals

Alan A. Cohen

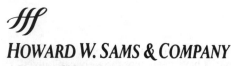

HOWARD W. SAMS & COMPANY
A Division of Macmillan, Inc.
4300 West 62nd Street
Indianapolis, Indiana 46268 USA

International Standard Book Number: 0-672-22678-2
Library of Congress Catalog Card Number: 89-62335

Acquisitions Editor: *Scott Arant*
Development Editor: *James Rounds*
Manuscript Editor: *Marie Butler-Knight*
Production Coordinator: *Marjorie Hopper*
Illustrators: *T. R. Emrick & Sally Copenhaver*
Cover Artist: *Ron Troxel*
Technical Reviewer: *Bruce Bartlett*
Compositor: *Cromer Graphics*

Printed in the United States of America

Trademarks

Contents

Preface

This text is designed for music students and others interested in audio technology. It assumes that the reader has some background knowledge of electronics. This book bridges the gap between this basic electronics understanding and its application to the field of audio engineering. (For those who do not yet have a background in electronics, there are many excellent texts on the subject.)

The first chapter, entitled *The Audio Chain*, presents an overview of a typical audio system. It includes an explanation of component interfacing and impedance matching.

Chapter 2, *Sound Measurement*, covers the decibel. This concept is described in simple language that a beginning mathematician can understand. The chapter covers the derivation of the unit and gives practical examples of its application.

In Chapter 3, basic information is given on op-amps. This provides the necessary background to an understanding of active components such as active filters, equalizers, mixers, and digital-to-analog converters.

Chapter 4 presents the pole/zero approach to analyzing the filtering effect of reactive components. Once this has been mastered, the concept of filtering becomes simple. Every upward slope can then be seen as a climb from a *zero*, and every downward slope as a descent from the high point of a *pole*. Passive filters are examined in Chapter 4, and active filters in Chapter 5.

Chapter 6, *Transformers*, discusses voltage changing, isolation, and impedance matching functions, and offers advice on avoiding transformer generated distortion. In the following chapter, semiconductor theory is explained, including the principles behind transistor amplification.

Chapter 8, *The Tape Recorder*, gives theoretical and practical information on tape recorders. The purpose of this chapter is to help you obtain good recordings even without professional equipment. This is followed by a chapter on the subject of digital audio. Chapter 9 includes a section on analog-to-digital interfacing and the process of digital recording. It   also discusses the characteristic performance of digital systems compared to analog systems.

Chapter 10, *Practical Audio Circuits*, then takes a close look at power supply, signal tracer, and mixer circuits. This chapter is designed to enable you to construct these useful devices. The final chapter offers valuable information on troubleshooting and maintenance of audio equipment, including a detailed tape recorder alignment procedure.

You will notice that diagrams have been included where it was thought helpful to do so. If an unfamiliar word or concept arises, its meaning can be discovered by reference to the glossary at the end of the book. And every effort has been made to clarify the concepts covered by using simple language and analogies taken from well understood situations.

1   The Audio Chain

1 The Audio Chain

Sound and Hearing

Sound consists of alternate high and low pressure waves moving through an elastic medium such as air. Sound can also be transmitted through any other elastic medium, such as water, steel, or rock. When sound waves in air strike a light surface, such as an eardrum or microphone diaphragm, the pressure fluctuations cause the diaphragm to fluctuate in proportion to the changing pressure. This enables the ear or microphone to convert the sound—in the case of the ear, into nerve impulses, and in the case of the microphone, into an electrical audio signal.

The sound source can be a vibrating or resonating object, such as a plucked guitar string, a struck tuning fork, or a cymbal. Each elastic object has its own fundamental resonant frequency; hence, a small bell resonates at a higher frequency than a large bell, and short piano strings at a higher frequency than long strings. The frequency is measured in cycles per second, sometimes called hertz (Hz). A hertz is the same as a cycle per second.

A simple object, such as a tuning fork, emits a pure sound at its fundamental (resonant) frequency. More complex objects, such as a bell or a drum, resonate not only at their own fundamental frequencies, but in some parts at whole number multiples of the fundamental. These higher frequencies are called *harmonics*. The relationship between frequency and harmonics is simple. The fundamental is called the first harmonic. The second harmonic is twice the fundamental frequency, the third harmonic is three times the fundamental, and so on. The word *high* is perfectly applicable to both frequency and pitch. If we compare the objective measurement of frequency with the subjective experience of the pitch of a tone, there is nearly a 100 percent correlation between them. A high frequency is experienced as a high pitched tone, a low frequency as a low pitched tone. The tonal parameters of human hearing are as follows:

- The lowest audible frequency is about 16 Hz.
- The highest audible frequency is about 16 kHz. (This varies. Some people can hear up to nearly 20 kHz; others only up to 10 kHz.)

Below the lowest audible frequency of 16 Hz, sound is experienced as a vibration or as individual thumps.

Another subjective relationship between pitch and frequency involves the recognition of the octave. It happens that double the frequency is perceived as one octave higher. So, an octave higher is twice the frequency and an octave lower is half the frequency of the original note.

There are two variables within the physical concept of sound. One that has already been mentioned is frequency. The other is the intensity or power of the sound wave. This depends on the sound pressure. The greater the pressure difference between the wave peaks and normal atmospheric pressure, the greater the intensity. Subjectively, this is experienced as loudness. Loudness can be measured as a pressure difference or as intensity, which is the corresponding acoustical power in watts per square centimeter.

The quietest audible sound occurs at an intensity of 10^{-16} W/cm^2. The loudest safe intensity is 10^{-4} W/cm^2. A louder sound causes hearing damage. Under these conditions, very fine sensory hairs in the inner ear get broken by the excessively loud sounds. The result is high frequency deafness. Unfortunately, during sound mixing and recording sessions, audio engineers tend to turn up their monitors to produce high sound intensities in the control room. Excessive loudness can also be experienced at some concerts. Under these conditions, hearing discomfort occurs or there is ringing in the ears. This is a warning sign. It means your hearing is being damaged and you are losing your high frequency hearing ability.

While it may not be acceptable to ask a long-time audio engineer to turn the monitors down, you can use earplugs or stuff a piece of tissue into each ear. The tissue will reduce the sound level by about 20 dB. (A dB is a unit of sound pressure or sound intensity level. It is described in Chapter 2.) Remember that if you misuse and destroy an amplifier or tape deck, you can purchase another (at a price). But if you destroy your hearing, you are stuck with it for the rest of your life. So be careful of your most sensitive audio equipment.

Now, let's return to consideration of some of the characteristics of sound. In the absence of harmonics, a pure tone corresponds to pressure fluctuations that oscillate with simple harmonic motion. This type of motion can be illustrated by viewing a point rotating around the circumference of a circle, as seen on edge so that only one dimension of movement is visible. Any purely vibrating elastic body, such as a tuning fork blade or guitar string, oscillates in this way. A graphical representation of such pressure changes on a time (or angular displacement) base is shown in Figure 1-1.

Fig. 1-1 Sine wave characteristics

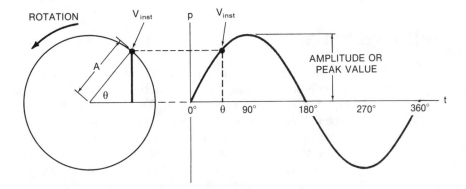

This characteristically shaped curve is called a *sine wave*, the reason being that (from the circular diagram on the left)

$$\left[\sin \theta = \frac{V_{inst}}{A} \right]$$

where

V_{inst} = Instantaneous value
A   = Amplitude
θ = Phase angle in degrees

From this equation, we arrive at

$$V_{inst} = A \sin \theta$$

So the value is always proportional to the sine of the angle.

As was mentioned earlier, musical instruments produce not only a pure fundamental note, but also harmonics. It is the relative proportional intensity of the different harmonics that causes what is known as the *timbre* of the instrument. This is what makes the difference between a Stradivarius and a cheap, mass-produced violin. However, most acoustical instruments produce a combination of harmonics that is pleasant to the ear.

An amplifier circuit also produces electrically generated harmonics. This is unfortunate, however, because an amplifier should reproduce exactly what is present and not add anything of its own. In addition, the electronically produced harmonics (unlike those produced by musical instruments) are objectionable and unpleasant to the ear. This effect is called distortion. Fortunately, present day amplifiers are being produced with a total harmonic distortion of less than 0.1 percent. You should try to avoid using equipment with total harmonic distortion of 1 percent or more. It is also important to avoid creating distortion by incorrect design or use of technical equipment. And this returns us to the main topic of this book.

Audio Systems

In a recording studio or in the sound reinforcement system for a performing group or orchestra, the sound isn't transferred from a single microphone directly to a tape recorder or power amplifier. There are usually a number of intermediate stages. This system forms a chain of audio components linked one after the other in series. The chain always starts and ends with a transducer.

A transducer is a component that converts nonelectrical energy into electrical energy or vice versa. At the start of the audio chain, there can be a microphone, a tape replay head, or a record playing cartridge. All of these are transducers. A microphone converts acoustical energy (sound pressure waves in air) into electrical energy in the form of a small fluctuating voltage. A record playing cartridge converts mechanical energy (due to movements of the stylus) into electrical energy. A magnetic replay head converts the combined effect of a fluctuating magnetic field and the mechanical energy of the moving tape into electrical energy.

At the other end of the audio chain, there are one or more loudspeakers. These transducers convert comparatively large quantities of electrical energy into acoustical energy, sufficient to fill a room or hall with sound. In this way, transducers start and terminate the audio chain. Briefly then, the audio chain is a series of audio components that process and amplify an audio signal.

The Audio Signal

Sound radiation consists of alternating high and low pressure waves. Figure 1-2 illustrates the instantaneous position of these waves as they travel outward from their source at the center. Their arrangement is similar to ripples on the surface of a pond into which a stone has been thrown, except that on a pond, these ripples lie on a two-dimensional surface to form expanding concentric circles, whereas sound waves form expanding concentric spheres moving outward from their source in all directions.

A microphone in the path of these waves would convert the changing air pressures to correspondingly changing voltages. A graph of the air pressure changes of a pure sound that passes a microphone could be plotted vertically against a time base, and would look like Figure 1-3(A). If the output voltage of this microphone were also plotted vertically on a time base, as in Figure 1-3(B), it would be seen that the voltage exactly corresponds to the air pressure at all times.

Fig. 1-2
Alternating high
and low pressure
waves

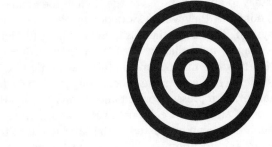

Fig. 1-3
Correspondence
between changing
pressure and
voltage

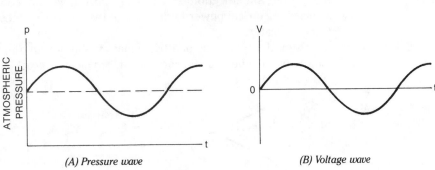

(A) Pressure wave   *(B) Voltage wave*

Similarly, for a complex wave, there would be equal correspondence between the pressure graph and the voltage graph, as seen in Figure 1-4.

Fig. 1-4
Correspondence
between pressure
and voltage in a
complex wave

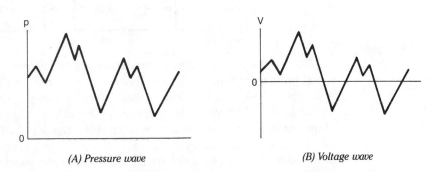

(A) Pressure wave   *(B) Voltage wave*

Such a fluctuating voltage produced by a microphone is called an audio *signal*. It is always an AC voltage because it fluctuates in both positive and negative directions. It is called a signal because, by definition, a signal transmits information. The audio signal transmits information about the air pressure changes of a traveling sound wave, and the information is encoded in the form of voltage. This voltage can, of course, be both processed and amplified under the skilled control of an audio engineer. This basic process is described in detail in the following chapters.

Back at the start of the audio chain, the microphone, tape head, or record playing cartridge all output very small voltages in the order of from 2 to 15 mV. It is necessary to amplify these voltages before they can be combined or processed. If this is not done, they will be swamped by electrical background noise generated in the system. Therefore, there is a pre-amplifier (designed to amplify very small signal voltages) immediately after the first transducer. Let us assume that the system starts with a microphone. In this case, it must be followed by a microphone pre-amplifier. Then comes the processing stage or stages. These could consist of an equalizer, compressor, or expander, mixing of other channels from other microphones, addition of echo or reverberation, and so forth. Finally, when the audio signal has been processed to the satisfaction of the audio engineer, comes the power amplification stage. This must give the completed audio signal sufficient electrical power to drive all of the speakers necessary to fill the room, hall, or theater.

Using the schematic of a triangular symbol for an amplifier and a rectangle for any other type of audio component, a typical audio chain might look like that shown in Figure 1-5.

Fig. 1-5 Typical audio chain

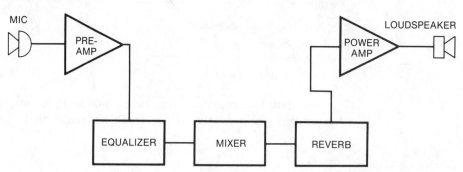

The only difference that occurs when digital systems are used is that the signal processing is done digitally. However, we inhabit an analog world, so the microphone input and the loudspeaker output have to remain in analog form. An analog-to-digital converter is therefore needed at the start of the processing part of the chain, and a digital-to-analog converter is needed at its end (see Figure 1-6).

To avoid confusion, I should mention that all active electronic devices are powered by DC sources. They are not powered by the audio signal. In Figure 1-5, the DC power that drives each component is not shown. It is assumed that the reader knows it exists. All that is illustrated is the audio signal path, from microphone to loudspeaker. In a detailed schematic of an amplifier or other electronic circuit (as in Figure 1-7), the DC source would be shown as a DC subcircuit running vertically, whereas the signal path, by convention, would be shown running horizontally.

To distinguish between the DC power supply and the AC audio signal, remember that the DC supply powers the electronic circuit and the AC audio signal controls its performance. In the case of a small, battery operated radio, the power supply is the battery. In the case of a 60 W amplifier, a battery would be

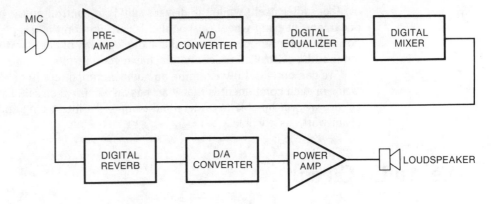

Fig. 1-6 Typical digital audio chain

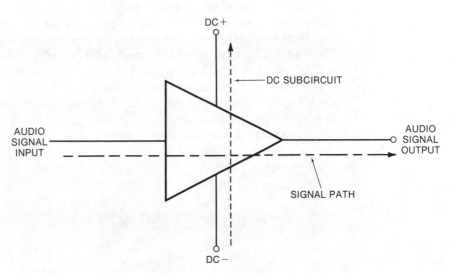

Fig. 1-7 Schematic of electronic circuit, showing DC subcircuit and signal path

insufficient, so it is powered by the 115 V, 60 Hz AC power line. In this case, the 115 V line supply is converted by an internal power supply circuit within the amplifier into a powerful DC source that can energize the amplifier to give out the necessary 60 W of sound.

As an analogy to this relationship, consider a car. When you sit in your car, it is not the movement of your foot on the gas pedal that powers the car. This merely controls the power output of the engine. The engine powers the car. Similarly, the audio signal supplies information to the amplifier and controls it, whereas the DC power supply produces the power.

Having said that, the fact is that there is a small, but important amount of electrical power at all stages of the audio signal. And it is this audio signal waveform, voltage, and power that we will be analyzing in detail in the future, because these are the characteristics that the audio engineer must control. The power supplied will then look after itself. In exactly the same way, the engine of a car looks after itself, while the driver's skill is in controlling the gas pedal, brake pedal, and steering wheel. Just as the driver's foot on the gas pedal requires low power but precise operation, so the audio signal is of comparatively low power, but must be controlled precisely to achieve good results.

We can now usefully examine an audio commponent in detail. The common factor in each component is that it acts as an electrical circuit. By examining this circuit, we will be able to understand component interfacing and how the audio chain works as a whole.

The Audio Circuit

Every circuit consists of a voltage source and a load. It is from the voltage source that the power, in the form of electrical energy, is derived. The load is that part of the circuit that uses the power and that the whole circuit is designed to operate. The load can be anything that is used and is driven by electricity. It can be an electric motor, a light bulb, a coffee maker, or an amplifier. However, in the circuit diagram, it can always be represented by a resistor, because it acts and absorbs power just as a resistor would. So, for calculation purposes, we think of it as a resistor of a given value.

All circuits fall into two natural parts:

1. The voltage source, or *generator* part of the circuit
2. The load

The simplest possible circuit would look like that in Figure 1-8.

Fig. 1-8 The simplest possible circuit

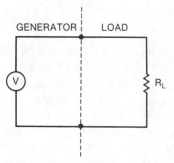

In practice, even the simplest circuit can never be this simple. The reason is that there is no generator, however large and powerful, that can supply all possible loads with a 100 percent constant voltage. Due to internal resistance within the generator, there is some voltage drop in the generating process when a load is connected. The more current that is drawn, the lower the generator output voltage becomes. In the case of mechanically driven generators powered by steam turbines, various factors and the actual resistance of the wiring of the rotor cause the output voltage to drop when a large amout of current is drawn. In the case of a battery, the speed at which the electrochemical reaction can take place depends on the voltage drop that the load produces at the terminals. So the greater the current drain, the greater this voltage drop has to be. Of course, a large battery can produce more current output than a small one for a given voltage drop. This simply means that there is less voltage drop due to internal resistance. But however large the battery, there will be some drop. And the drop will increase in proportion to the current.

This situation, in which the voltage drop is proportional to the current, is exactly what happens when current flows through a resistor. The voltage drop can be calculated by Ohm's Law, from the relationship

$$V = IR$$

where
V = Voltage drop
I = Current drawn
R = Resistance

As a result, any generator has to be considered as having an internal resistance (sometimes called its output resistance). The larger the generator, the lower will be its output resistance, because it can output more current for a given voltage drop. But in all cases, some internal resistance must be included for calculation purposes. So the simplest practical circuit becomes a voltage source with two resistors in series. The internal resistance of the generator is included in the generator part of the circuit, as shown in Figure 1-9.

Fig. 1-9 Simplest practical circuit

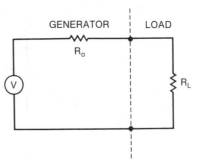

The internal resistance of the generator (signifying output resistance) is labeled R_o, because we will shortly be talking about the input resistance of an amplifier. If the internal resistance and the input resistance were both labeled R_i, there would be ambiguity. This circuit represents the fundamental behavior of all audio circuits.

If we consider a single audio component, isolated from all others, its output terminals being left open (with no load connected), then we can think of this audio component as entirely made up of three parts. This fact applies to all audio components except transducers. It applies to mixers, amplifiers, filters, equalizers, tape recorders, and so on. The three parts are

1. The *input resistance*, R_i (sometimes called the input impedance). This forms the effective resistance between the input terminal and ground. It is not made up of a single resistor, but it acts as one. So it can be considered a single resistance for calculation purposes.
2. The *signal voltage*, V. This forms the voltage source of the generator part of the circuit.
3. The *output resistance* of the *generator* part of the circuit, R_o (sometimes called the output impedance of the component). Again, it is not a single resistor, but it acts as one and can be so considered for calculation purposes.

The three parts of an audio component are shown in Figure 1-10. The realization that all audio components are made up of these three parts makes it simple to achieve correct impedance matching when interfacing an audio chain, or in any other required situation.

Fig. 1-10 The three parts of an audio component

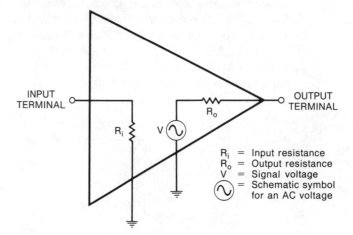

R_i = Input resistance
R_o = Output resistance
V = Signal voltage
= Schematic symbol for an AC voltage

Interfacing

Let us consider a simple audio chain consisting of a mic, pre-amplifier, equalizer, power amplifier, and loudspeaker. The three parts of each component fit together as illustrated in Figure 1-11.

Fig. 1-11 The relationship between the parts of each component in an audio chain

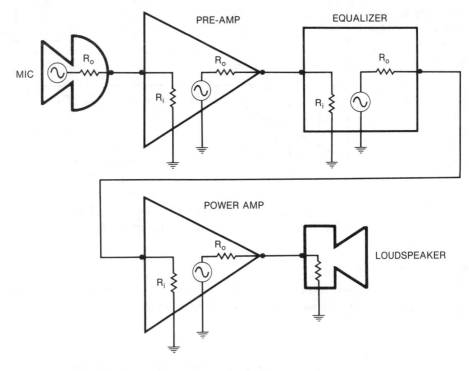

The key to understanding the interfacing situation is to think of each audio component in terms of these three essential parts:

- The input resistance
- The audio signal
- The output resistance

Notice that the input resistance of the pre-amplifier acts as the load for the microphone. The input resistance of the equalizer acts as the load for the pre-amplifier. The input resistance of the power amplifier acts as the load for the equalizer. This relationship is valid for the interface between any two components in an audio chain. In general, the input resistance of one component acts as the load for the previous component. You could say that the load for any component is the input resistance of the following stage; thus, two adjoining stages form a single audio circuit, linking them in an interrelated unity. As an example, let us examine the interface between component A and component B in Figure 1-12. We can assume that all ground symbols are connected. (All being at 0 volts, they act as though they are connected.) So the equivalent interfacing audio circuit consists of that shown in Figure 1-12, where:

R_oA = Output resistance of component A
R_iB = Input resistance of component B

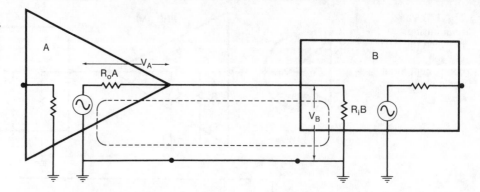

Fig. 1-12 Audio circuit created by interfacing

As you know, the current is the same in all parts of a series circuit. Call this value I. So by Ohm's law, the voltage lost across R_oA, namely V_A, is given by

$$V_A = IR_{oA} \qquad (1\text{-}1)$$

and the signal voltage that remains at the input terminal of the next stage, V_B, which would be across R_iB, is given by

$$V_B = IR_{iB} \qquad (1\text{-}2)$$

For best impedance matching, less than one-tenth of the signal voltage should be lost at the interface. This means that the signal voltage that remains at the input of the second stage, V_B, should be at least ten times that which is lost across the output resistance of the first stage, V_A. Thus,

$$V_B \geq 10\, V_A \qquad (1\text{-}3)$$

Substituting in Equation 1-3 for V_A and V_B from Equations 1-1 and 1-2,

$$IR_{iB} \geq 10\, R_{oA}$$

But I cancels, so

$$R_{iB} \geq 10\, R_{oA}$$

In other words, for good impedance matching, the input resistance of any stage should be at least ten times that of the output resistance of the previous stage. Very often the quantities are specified as *impedances* rather than *resistances*, but the same rule applies:

> For good impedance matching, the input impedance of one stage should be at least ten times that of the output impedance of the previous stage.

Problem 1-1: What minimum input impedance would be needed in a microphone pre-amplifier, if the mic's output impedance is 200 Ω?

Answer: Because R_i has to be ten times the value of R_o of the previous component, pre-amp R_i = at least $10 \times 200 \ \Omega$ = 2 kΩ. An input impedance of 2 kΩ or more would be suitable.

I have just described what is called *constant voltage* coupling, forming a constant voltage circuit. It is called constant voltage because, if $R_L \geq 10 \ R_o$, the voltage across the load will not have dropped more than 10 percent from its maximum value. So the voltage across the load will be between 90 and 100 percent of its maximum value. Maximum voltage occurs when $R_L = \infty$, or under open circuit conditions. Then there is no current through R_o and no voltage drop across it, so the terminal voltage equals the source voltage.

When audio component (2), the load in Figure 1-13, is connected across the output terminals of component (1) in an audio chain, the input resistance of component (2) acts as the load for component (1). And because current now flows through the circuit, there is a voltage drop across R_o and the resultant voltage across the terminals drops. Thus, V_L is always less than V_s. The amount of the voltage drop due to the insertion of this component is called the *insertion loss*. Using constant voltage coupling impedances ($R_L \geq 10 \ R_o$), this insertion loss is kept small.

Fig. 1-13
Component
interfacing

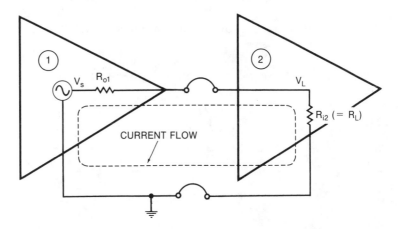

There is another type of coupling called *power matched*. This occurs when the load resistance equals the generator output resistance ($R_L = R_o$). Then, for a given source voltage, V_s, the maximum possible amount of power is transferred to the load. In general, it can be stated that:

Maximum power is transferred to the load when the load resistance equals the source resistance.

This is called power matched coupling. The power in the load could be calculated from

$$P_L = I^2 R_L$$

But by Ohm's Law,

$$I = \frac{V_s}{R_o + R_L}$$

so,

$$P_L = \frac{V_s^2 R_L}{(R_o + R_L)^2}$$

If we take, as an example, a source voltage of 1 V,

$$P_L = \frac{R_L}{(R_o + R_L)^2}$$

Fig. 1-14
Variation of P_L as R_L changes with a constant voltage source

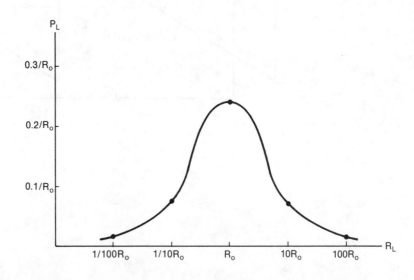

A graph, shown in Figure 1-14, is plotted on a logarithmic base of P_L for various values of R_L as a proportion of R_o, using a 1 V source. It can be seen that precisely when $R_L = R_o$, the power reaches a maximum. So coupling between components in an audio chain can be specified in two ways:

1. Constant voltage coupling, when $R_L \geq 10 \times R_o$
2. Power matched coupling, when $R_L = R_o$

This chapter has been devoted to a general view of audio systems. In the next chapter, the basic audio measurement unit, the decibel, will be defined and its relationship to other units will be described.

2 Sound Measurement

2 Sound Measurement

Intensity

Consider a point source of sound in the form of a small, vibrating object such as a tuning fork, bell, or small loudspeaker cone. The mechanical vibrations produce pressure waves in the air, which travel outward in all directions. The amount of mechanical work done per unit of time (in one second) in generating these pressure waves is the total acoustical power being generated.

At a given distance d from the sound source, there is a spherical surface (of radius d) through which all of the sound energy passes. It is clear that only a small part of the total sound passes through one square centimeter of this area (see Figure 2-1). This is the intensity of the sound at this distance.

Fig. 2-1
Proportion of sound radiation that strikes 1 cm² of area

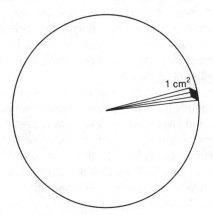

Sound intensity is defined as the acoustical power per unit area of surface onto which the sound strikes. Thus,

$$I = P/A$$

where
  I = Intensity in watts per sq cm
  P = Total acoustical power in watts
  A = Area in cm^2

Numerically, this amounts to the total acoustical power being radiated, divided by the total surface area of this sphere. (The surface of a sphere of radius *R* is given by $4\pi R^2$.) Therefore, the intensity at distance *d* is given by

$$I = \frac{P}{4\pi d^2}$$

For a steady-state, continuously generated sound, P remains constant, and both 4 and π are also constants. So it can be seen that the sound intensity at distance *d* from the source is proportional to $1/d^2$. Thus, the intensity of a given sound diminishes as the square of its distance from the source. This is called the *Inverse Square Law*. It applies to any quantity that radiates in all directions from a point source—to radio transmissions, light intensity, gravitational field strength, and so forth.

Bel and Decibel

Dynamic range is the ratio of the loudest to quietest sound intensity that can be produced or accepted without distortion or damage to the system. In an electronic component such as an amplifier, the high end of this parameter is the loudest sound that can be produced, just below overload distortion level. The low end is the noise level. Any quieter sound is swallowed up by the internally generated noise. In a good quality analog tape recorder, the dynamic range is about one million (10^6) to one.

The human ear is a more marvelous instrument. It has a dynamic range that extends from the quietest audible sound intensity of 10^{-16} W/cm^2 to the loudest sound just below the level that causes pain and damage to the ear. This maximum loudness occurs at an intensity of 10^{-4} W/cm^2. So the dynamic range of the human ear is 10^{-4} to 10^{-16}, namely 10^{12}. This quantity, one trillion, is a million times greater than that of a normal man-made machine. It exceeds the dynamic range of the best possible amplifier, which is 10^{10}. The ear has a hundred times the dynamic range of a good amplifier.

Because of the vast dynamic range of the human ear, it is more convenient to measure sound intensity by exponents of 10 (logarithms) than by numbers on a

HOWARD W. SAMS & COMPANY

Bookmark

DEAR VALUED CUSTOMER:

Howard W. Sams & Company is dedicated to bringing you timely and authoritative books for your personal and professional library. Our goal is to provide you with excellent technical books written by the most qualified authors. You can assist us in this endeavor by checking the box next to your particular areas of interest.

We appreciate your comments and will use the information to provide you with a more comprehensive selection of titles.

Thank you,

Vice President, Book Publishing
Howard W. Sams & Company

COMPUTER TITLES:

Hardware
- ☐ Apple 140
- ☐ Macintosh 101
- ☐ Commodore 110
- ☐ IBM & Compatibles 114

Business Applications
- ☐ Word Processing J01
- ☐ Data Base J04
- ☐ Spreadsheets J02

Operating Systems
- ☐ MS-DOS K05
- ☐ OS/2 K10
- ☐ CP/M K01
- ☐ UNIX K03

Programming Languages
- ☐ C L03
- ☐ Pascal L05
- ☐ Prolog L12
- ☐ Assembly L01
- ☐ BASIC L02
- ☐ HyperTalk L14

Troubleshooting & Repair
- ☐ Computers S05
- ☐ Peripherals S10

Other
- ☐ Communications/Networking M03
- ☐ AI/Expert Systems T18

ELECTRONICS TITLES:
- ☐ Amateur Radio T01
- ☐ Audio T03
- ☐ Basic Electronics T20
- ☐ Basic Electricity T21
- ☐ Electronics Design T12
- ☐ Electronics Projects T04
- ☐ Satellites T09

- ☐ Instrumentation T05
- ☐ Digital Electronics T11

Troubleshooting & Repair
- ☐ Audio S11
- ☐ Television S04
- ☐ VCR S01
- ☐ Compact Disc S02
- ☐ Automotive S06
- ☐ Microwave Oven S03

Other interests or comments: _____

_____

Name_____

Title _____

Company _____

Address _____

City _____

State/Zip _____

Daytime Telephone No. _____

A Division of Macmillan, Inc.

4300 West 62nd Street   Indianapolis, Indiana 46268   22678

Bookmark

sf

HOWARD W. SAMS
& COMPANY

linear scale. Therefore, the scientists at the Bell Laboratories, earlier this century, created a unit of sound measurement based on the use of exponents (logarithms). This unit of sound measurement is the *bel* which is equal to the exponent (log) of the ratio of the intensity of a sound, to a reference intensity. The reference intensity is the lowest threshold of human hearing, which is 10^{-16} W/cm². So if a sound intensity of 10^{-11} W/cm² were to be measured, its level with respect to the reference value would be given by

$$\text{Intensity level, L} = \log \frac{10^{-11}}{10^{-16}}$$

$$\frac{10^{-11}}{10^{-16}} = 10^{-11} \times 10^{+16} = 10^5$$

So,

$$L = \log 10^5$$
$$= 5 \text{ bels}$$

A level is usually designated by the uppercase letter L with appropriate subscript. Intensity level would, therefore, be given by

$$L_I = \log \frac{I}{I_{ref}} \text{ bels}$$

where

L_I = Intensity level in bels
I = Intensity in W/cm²
I_{ref} = Reference intensity in W/cm²

In practice, a smaller unit was needed, so the bel was divided into tenths. A tenth of a bel is called a decibel (dB). Using this unit, the intensity level would be given by

$$L_I = 10 \log \frac{I}{I_{ref}} \text{ dB}$$

Problem 2-1: What is the intensity level of a sound of 10^{-7} W/cm²?

Answer: $L_I = 10 \log \dfrac{I}{I_{ref}}$

$$= 10 \log \frac{10^{-7}}{10^{-16}}$$

$$= 10 \log 10^9$$

$$= 10 \times 9$$

$$= 90 \text{ dB}$$

Problem 2-2:   What is the maximum safe intensity level that can be accepted by the human ear? Intensity above 10^{-4} W/cm² causes hearing damage.

Answer: $L_I = 10 \log \dfrac{10^{-4}}{10^{-16}}$

$$= 10 \log 10^{12}$$

$$= 10 \times 12$$

$$= 120 \text{ dB}$$

Power Level and Level Gain

Because sound intensity is a measure of acoustical power per unit area, and because the unit of area is constant, it follows that intensity is directly proportional to power. Thus, $I = K \times P$ and $I_{ref} = K \times P_{ref}$, where K is the constant of proportionality. So,

$$\frac{I}{I_{ref}} = \frac{K\,P}{K\,P_{ref}} = \frac{P}{P_{ref}}$$

This means that power can be evaluated as a level, in the same way as sound intensity (and sound pressure). In practice, this is more useful to audio engineers, because modern technology utilizes the power from an amplifier to achieve the required acoustical effect.

Not only power, but also voltage can be evaluated in dB units; in fact, the dB unit is the most useful way for signal levels to be specified. The manufacturer of a microphone or some other piece of audio equipment is likely to supply a graphical representation of the equipment's performance by plotting the output level in dB units against a frequency base plotted horizontally. Thus, the user can see at which frequency the output has fallen by 3 dB, and also between which frequency parameters the output is flat within, say, 2 dB. I mention 2 dB because 2 dB is the smallest level change that can be detected by the human ear. A change of less than 2 dB is inaudible.

Any quantity can be evaluated in dB units by taking the logarithm of the ratio of the value to a reference value. But we will concentrate on the evaluation of electrical power, voltage, and pressure in dB, because these are the quantities most often used in audio technology. To evaluate power in terms of a level, we start with the equation for determining intensity level.

$$L_I = 10 \log \frac{I}{I_{ref}} \text{ dB}$$

We then replace the intensity ratio with the corresponding and numerically equal power ratio.

$$L_P = 10 \log \frac{P}{P_{ref}} \text{ dB}$$

This gives the power level. P_{ref} is a reference power that does not necessarily correspond to the reference intensity, because various sound transducers work at different efficiencies. All that is required is that the reference power be standardized. This is taken almost universally as 1 mW. Therefore,

$$L_P = 10 \log \frac{P}{1 \text{ mW}} \text{ dBm} \tag{2-1}$$

The unit is specified as dBm to indicate that the reference value is 1 mW. Note that a negative value of dBm does *not* mean a negative power. It means that the level is below the reference level of 1 mW.

Problem 2-3: What is the power level of 2.8 W?

Answer: $L_P = 10 \log \dfrac{P}{P_{ref}}$

$$= 10 \log \frac{2.8}{.001}$$

Note that the numerator and denominator of the fraction must both be stated in the same units—in this case, watts. So,

$L_P = 10 \log 2800$
$\quad = 10 \times 3.45$
$\quad = 34.5 \text{ dBm}$

Problem 2-4: Convert a power of 0.25 mW to a power level.

Answer: $L_P = 10 \log \dfrac{.25}{1}$

Note that mW is now being used; therefore, the reference power must also be in mW (1, not .001 as in the previous problem).

$L_P = 10 \log 0.25$
$\quad = 10 \times (-.602)$
$\quad = -6.02 \text{ dBm}$

(See supplementary problem 2-1A at the end of this chapter.)

You may wonder why electrical power and voltage are not specified in watts and volts. There are two reasons. First, it is much easier to calculate the effect of passing the audio signal through a number of audio components, if amplification of each is specified in decibels. This is because decibels, being exponents, can be added, whereas a signal voltage must be multiplied by the corresponding voltage gains. Mathematical examples of this are given later in this chapter. The other and perhaps most important reason why the use of dB units is preferred in audio technology relates to the characteristics of human hearing. It happens that the ear's response to sound intensity change is logarithmic. Because decibels are also logarithmic, a person's experience of changes in loudness exactly corresponds to the dB changes; but they do not correspond linearly to the changes of acoustical power or voltage. So a signal voltage change is misleading as to the audible result, whereas the numerical value of the dB change precisely evaluates the subjective effect of this change in loudness.

As mentioned, the subjective experience of a change of loudness is logarithmic. This means that at low intensity listening levels, a very small increase in acoustical power produces a greater experience of loudness increase than the same power increase would produce at high intensity levels. Hence, there is a saying that at low listening levels you can hear a pin drop. The same increase of sound would be undetectable at high listening levels.

Examples have already been given of the conversion of power in watts to a power level in dBm units. Power gain can also be converted to a corresponding level gain in dB units.

The power gain of an amplifier is defined as the ratio of its output power to its input power. Because all of the amplifier's output power goes into the load, the output power of an amplifier is often called the *load power*, specified as P_L. Its power gain is given by the formula

$$G_P = \frac{P_L}{P_i}$$

or

$$G_P = \frac{P_o}{P_i}$$

where

G_P = Power gain
P_L or P_o = Power in the load, or output power
P_i = Input power

When you divide logarithmic numbers, their logs are subtracted. Decibels are logarithmic values; consequently, the corresponding power *level* gains are given by

$$L_{PG} = L_{PL} - L_{Pi} \qquad \text{(2-2)}$$

where
  L_{PG} = Power level gain
  L_{PL} = Output power level
  L_{Pi} = Input power level

However,

$$L_{PL} = 10 \log \frac{P_L}{P_{ref}}$$

and

$$L_{Pi} = 10 \log \frac{P_i}{P_{ref}}$$

Substituting these two expressions in Equation 2-2,

$$L_{PG} = L_{PL} - L_{Pi}$$

becomes

$$L_{PG} = 10 \log \frac{P_L}{P_{ref}} - 10 \log \frac{P_i}{P_{ref}}$$

So,

$$L_{PG} = 10 \left(\log \frac{P_L}{P_{ref}} - \log \frac{P_i}{P_{ref}} \right)$$

$$= 10 \log \frac{\dfrac{P_L}{P_{ref}}}{\dfrac{P_i}{P_{ref}}}$$

$$= 10 \log \left(\frac{P_L}{P_{ref}} \times \frac{P_{ref}}{P_i} \right)$$

Therefore,

$$L_{PG} = 10 \log \frac{P_L}{P_i} \qquad \text{(2-3)}$$

Thus the power level gain can be found in two ways, depending on the data available.

$$L_{PG} = 10 \log \frac{P_L}{P_i} \text{ dB}$$

or

$$L_{PG} = 10 \log Gp \text{ dB}$$

These methods require that the input and output power (or power gain) be known. Alternatively, it can be found from the difference in levels. In this case, the formula $L_{PG} = L_{PL} - L_{Pi}$ dB can be used, provided the input and output power *levels* are known.

Sound Pressure and Pressure Level

The loudness of sound can be measured not only by its intensity, but also by what is called its pressure. Sound pressure is the difference between normal atmospheric pressure and the average instantaneous magnitude of the pressure of the sound wave. The louder the sound, the greater the difference in pressure between the peaks and troughs of the sound wave. The *sound pressure level* (SPL) is this value converted to dB units. The lowest threshold of human hearing is taken as the reference pressure. It is also taken as the reference intensity. The result is that pressure level is always numerically equal to intensity level. We can state, for instance, that the lowest level of human hearing is both an intensity level and a pressure level of 0 dB. The loudest safe audible sound is an intensity level and pressure level of 120 dB.

The relationship between power and pressure is not linear. A power gain is proportional to the square of the corresponding pressure gain. This is because power is the product of force times distance moved per unit time. Not only does pressure gain increase the force, it also causes molecular movement to increase. (This is what forms the pressure wave.) So an increase in pressure causes an increase in both force and distance moved. This is why a power increase is proportional to the *square* of the pressure increase.

An intensity ratio then equals the square of the corresponding pressure ratio. If sound pressure level is to be calculated, we start by writing the formula for intensity level.

$$L_I = 10 \log \frac{I}{I_{ref}}$$

We then replace the intensity ratio with the numerically equal square of the pressure ratio.

$$\text{SPL (sound pressure level)} = 10 \log \left(\frac{p}{p_{ref}} \right)^2$$

But, by the laws of exponents,

$$\log a^2 = 2 \log a$$

Therefore,

$$\text{SPL} = 10 \times 2 \log \frac{p}{p_{\text{ref}}}$$

Consequently,

$$\text{SPL} = 20 \log \frac{p}{p_{\text{ref}}} \text{ dB} \qquad \text{(2-4)}$$

Note that lowercase p is used to denote pressure, while uppercase P is used to denote power. The pressure that corresponds to the lowest threshold of human hearing is 20 micropascals. (A pascal, Pa, is 1 newton per square meter.) And the highest safe audible sound pressure is 20 Pa. So the maximum safe sound pressure level (SPL) is given by

$$\text{SPL}_{\text{max}} = 20 \log \frac{20}{20 \times 10^{-6}}$$

$$= 20 \log 10^6$$
$$= 20 \times 6$$
$$= 120 \text{ dB}$$

A different unit of pressure sometimes used in microphone specifications is the *bar* (1 bar $= 10^5$ Pa). Using this unit, the lowest threshold of human hearing is a sound pressure of 2×10^{-10} bar (that is, 2×10^{-4} μbar). The maximum safe sound pressure is 2×10^{-4} bar, and the maximum safe SPL can be found from

$$\text{SPL}_{\text{max}} = 20 \log \frac{2 \times 10^{-4}}{2 \times 10^{-10}}$$

$$= 20 \log 10^6$$
$$= 20 \times 6$$
$$= 120 \text{ dB}$$

Because intensity reference and sound pressure reference (in whatever units) are both taken as the lowest threshold of human hearing, the maximum safe levels are identical, namely 120 dB. Similarly, the lowest threshold of audible sound is identical in each case, namely 0 dB. The advantage of working with dB units shows itself here, in that it is only necessary to remember that audible sound parameters extend from 0 dB to 120 dB, whether the original units are in intensity or pressure.

Most professional microphones are specified as having a maximum permissible SPL of 135 dB. This covers the audible range of 120 dB with 15 dB clearance.

Sometimes it is helpful to use as a reference point the SPL that corresponds to 1 Pa or 1 μbar. These can be found from the fact that SPL is calculated as

$$SPL = 20 \log \frac{p}{p_{ref}}$$

Therefore, 1 Pa gives a value of

$$SPL = 20 \log \frac{1}{2 \times 10^{-5}} = 94 \text{ dB}$$

And 1 μbar gives a value of

$$SPL = 20 \log \frac{10^{-6}}{2 \times 10^{-10}} = 74 \text{ dB}$$

Both of these values approximate the actual SPL occurring in a studio during sound recording.

To summarize, the lowest threshold of human hearing is evaluated as

1. An *intensity* of 10^{-16} W/cm^2 = L_I of 0 dB
2. A *pressure* of 20 μPa = SPL of 0 dB
3. A *pressure* of 2×10^{-10} bar = SPL of 0 dB

The highest safe threshold of human hearing is evaluated as

1. An *intensity* of 10^{-4} W/cm^2 = L_I of 120 dB
2. A *pressure* of 20 Pa = SPL of 120 dB
3. A *pressure* of 2×10^{-4} bar = SPL of 120 dB

Voltage Level and Level Gain

Most electronic measurements are made in voltages for convenience. The relationship between voltage and power in any load R is given by

$$P = \frac{V^2}{R} \tag{2-5}$$

Thus, the power gain experienced by a load (such as a loudspeaker), in which the power increases from P_2 to P_1, is given by the equation

$$G_P = \frac{P_1}{P_2} \tag{2-6}$$

Substituting in Equation 2-6 for P_1 and P_2 from the relationship in Equation 2-5, the power ratio in Equation 2-6 can be written

$$\frac{P_1}{P_2} = \frac{\frac{V_1^2}{R}}{\frac{V_2^2}{R}}$$

$$= \frac{V_1^2}{R} \times \frac{R}{V_2^2}$$

$$= \frac{V_1^2}{V_2^2}$$

$$= \left(\frac{V_1}{V_2}\right)^2$$

Thus,

$$\frac{P_1}{P_2} = \left(\frac{V_1}{V_2}\right)^2 \tag{2-7}$$

So it can be stated that, for a constant load, the power ratio equals the voltage ratio squared. That is,

$$\text{Power Ratio} = (\text{Voltage Ratio})^2$$

It is now not only possible to express intensity, power, and pressure as a level or level gain, it is equally possible to express voltage as a voltage level or level gain. To do so, we merely have to replace the power ratio with the square of the voltage ratio. We start by rewriting the two equations for power level and level gain.

$$L_P = 10 \log \frac{P}{P_{ref}} \qquad\qquad L_{PG} = 10 \log \frac{P_L}{P_i}$$

Replacing the power ratio in each equation with the corresponding square of the voltage ratio,

$$L_V = 10 \log \left(\frac{V}{V_{ref}}\right)^2 \qquad\qquad L_{VG} = 10 \log \left(\frac{V_L}{V_i}\right)^2$$

These can be written

$$L_V = 20 \log \frac{V}{V_{ref}} \qquad\qquad L_{VG} = 20 \log \frac{V_L}{V_i}$$

Just as power level gain can be found from either

$$10 \log \frac{P_L}{P_i} \qquad\qquad \text{or} \qquad\qquad L_{PL} - L_{Pi}$$

so voltage level can be found from either

$$20 \log \frac{V_L}{V_i} \qquad\qquad \text{or} \qquad\qquad L_{VL} - L_{Vi}$$

The Standard Audio Circuit

In order to determine the most suitable value for V_{ref}, it was decided to use a standard audio circuit, shown in Figure 2-2, with a standard load of 600 Ω. Then the reference voltage would be the voltage that produces the reference power of 1 mW in this standard load.

Fig. 2-2 The standard audio circuit

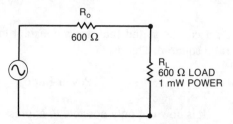

Using the same mathematical relationship between voltage, power, and resistance,

$$P = \frac{V^2}{R}$$

we see that

$$V^2 = PR$$

Therefore,

$$V = \sqrt{PR}$$

Substituting the values of P and R in the standard audio circuit load gives us

$$V_{ref} = \sqrt{.001 \times 600}$$
$$= \sqrt{0.6}$$
$$= .775 \text{ V}$$

Thus, V_{ref} is usually taken as 0.775 V, and the voltage level can be found from the formula

$$L_V = 20 \log \frac{V}{.775} \text{ dBv}$$

(The unit is specified as dBv to indicate that the value is related to a reference voltage of 0.775 V.)

Levels can be thought of as relating to a reference value. Just as we think of a river level being above or below its normal level, in the same way we can think of a voltage level or power level as a number of decibels above or below the reference level. So a voltage level of − 6 dBv does *not* mean a negative voltage. It means 6 dB below the reference value. Similarly, 0 dBm does not mean zero power. It means that the power level is at the reference power level (which is 1 mW).

Problem 2-5:   What voltage level corresponds to 24 V?

Answer: $L_V = 20 \log \frac{V}{.775}$

$$= 20 \log \frac{24}{.775}$$

$$= 20 \log 31$$

$$= 20 \times 1.49$$

$$= 29.8 \text{ dBv}$$

Problem 2-6:   Convert 15 mV to a voltage level.

Answer: $L_V = 20 \log \frac{V}{.775}$

$$= 20 \log \frac{.015}{.775}$$

$$= 20 \log .0194$$

$$= 20 \times (-1.71)$$

$$= -34.3 \text{ dBv}$$

(See supplementary problem 2-4A.)

dB Applications

The reference voltage is chosen to correspond to the reference power across a standard load of 600 Ω. It is only in a load of this value that the voltage level is numerically equal to the power level. It is important to remember this.

The voltage level numerically equals the power level when, and only when, the load resistor is 600 ohms.

With any other load resistance, these two values are no longer numerically equal. This is because the power produced by a given voltage is not the same across different resistors. A given voltage across low resistance produces more power than it does across high resistance. The level difference that results can be calculated by a formula that will be derived later. Note that powers, voltages, and gains are always multiplied or divided as shown below.

$$\text{Power gain, } G_p = \frac{P_L}{P_i} \qquad \text{and} \qquad \text{Voltage gain, } G_V = \frac{V_L}{V_i}$$

or

$$P_L = P_i \times G_P \qquad \text{and} \qquad V_L = V_i \times G_V$$

or

$$P_i = \frac{P_L}{G_P} \qquad \text{and} \qquad V_i = \frac{V_L}{G_V}$$

Levels, however, are added or subtracted (never multiplied or divided) as follows:

$$L_{PG} = L_{PL} - L_{Pi} \qquad \text{and} \qquad L_{VG} = L_{VL} - L_{Vi}$$

or

$$L_{PL} = L_{Pi} + L_{PG} \qquad \text{and} \qquad L_{VL} = L_{Vi} + L_{VG}$$

or

$$L_{Pi} = L_{PL} - L_{PG} \qquad \text{and} \qquad L_{Vi} = L_{VL} - L_{VG}$$

This is because levels are exponents. When mathematical powers of a given base are multiplied or divided, the exponents (logs) are added or subtracted. (See supplementary problems 2-9A, 2-10A, and 2-11A.)

Problem 2-7: Find the power level gain of this amplifier:

0.5 W   9.5 W

Answer:

$$L_{PG} = 10 \log \frac{P_L}{P_i}$$

$$= 10 \log \frac{9.5}{0.5}$$

$$= 10 \log 19$$

$$= 10 \times 1.28$$

$$= 12.8 \text{ dB}$$

(See supplementary problem 2-2A.)

Problem 2-8: (a) Find the input and output voltage levels of the following amplifier.

(b) Find the voltage level gain of the amplifier.

623 mV   8.3 V

Answer:

(a)
$$L_{Vi} = 20 \log \frac{V_i}{.775} \qquad L_{VL} = 20 \log \frac{V_L}{.775}$$

$$= 20 \log \frac{.623}{.775} \qquad\quad = 20 \log \frac{8.3}{.775}$$

$$= 20 \log 0.804 \qquad\quad = 20 \log 10.7$$

$$= 20 \times (-.095) \qquad\quad = 20 \times 1.03$$

$$= -1.9 \text{ dBv} \qquad\qquad = 20.6 \text{ dBv}$$

(b) Because both the input and output voltages and also the input and output voltage levels are known, the voltage level gain can be found in two ways.

Using V_i and V_L: Using L_{Vi} and L_{VL}:

$$L_{VG} = 20 \log \frac{V_L}{V_i} \qquad L_{VG} = L_{VL} - L_{Vi}$$

$$= 20 \log \frac{8.3}{.623} \qquad\quad = 20.6 - (-1.9)$$

$$= 20 \log 13.4 \qquad\qquad = 22.5 \text{ dB}$$
$$= 22.5 \text{ dB}$$

(See supplementary problems 2-3A and 2-10A.)

If it should be necessary to convert a power level or voltage level to a power or voltage, the relationship can be manipulated as follows:

$$L_P = 10 \log \frac{P}{.001}$$

Divide both sides by 10.

$$\frac{L_P}{10} = \log \frac{P}{.001}$$

Antilog both sides.

$$10^{\frac{L_P}{10}} = \frac{P}{.001}$$

Multiply both sides by .001.

$$P = .001 \times 10^{\frac{L_P}{10}}$$

where P = power in watts.

$$L_V = 20 \log \frac{V}{.775}$$

Divide both sides by 20.

$$\frac{L_V}{20} = \log \frac{V}{.775}$$

Antilog both sides.

$$10^{\frac{L_V}{20}} = \frac{V}{.775}$$

Multiply both sides by .775.

$$V = .775 \times 10^{\frac{L_V}{20}}$$

where V = voltage in volts

(Note that $10^{\frac{L_P}{10}}$ is the antilog of $\frac{L_P}{10}$, and $10^{\frac{L_V}{20}}$ is the antilog of $\frac{L_V}{20}$.
(See supplementary problems 2-5A and 2-7A.)

Where a power level gain or voltage level gain has to be converted to a power gain (power ratio) or voltage gain (voltage ratio), the derivation of the required equation is:

$$L_{PG} = 10 \log \frac{P_L}{P_i}$$

Divide both sides by 10.

$$\frac{L_{PG}}{10} = \log \frac{P_L}{P_i}$$

Antilog both sides.

$$\frac{P_L}{P_i} = 10^{\frac{L_{PG}}{10}}$$

or $G_p = 10^{\frac{L_{PG}}{10}}$

$$L_{VG} = 20 \log \frac{V_L}{V_i}$$

Divide both sides by 20.

$$\frac{L_{VG}}{20} = \log \frac{V_L}{V_i}$$

Antilog both sides.

$$\frac{V_L}{V_i} = 10^{\frac{L_{VG}}{20}}$$

or $G_V = 10^{\frac{L_{VG}}{20}}$

(See supplementary problem 2-8A.)

Problem 2-9:   Find the voltage that would be represented by 17 dBv.

Answer: $V = .775 \times 10^{\frac{L_V}{20}}$

$= .775 \times 10^{\frac{17}{20}}$

$= .775 \times 10^{.85}$

$= .775 \times 7.08$

$= 5.49 \text{ V}$

Problem 2-10:   What amplifier power gain corresponds to a power level gain of 14.5 dB?

Answer: $G_P = 10^{\frac{L_P}{10}}$

$= 10^{\frac{14.5}{10}}$

$= 10^{1.45}$

$= 28.2$

(See supplementary problems 2-6A and 2-7A.)

Although the mathematical derivation of dB units appears complex, their use is simple. It is only necessary to add them where level gains are being added, or subtract them to find the difference between two levels. Mathematically, nothing could be easier.

Problem 2-11:   What is the voltage level at the output of this amplifier?

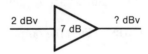

Answer: $L_{VL} = 2 + 7 = 9 \text{ dBv}$

Problem 2-12:   What input power level would produce 23 dBm at the output of this amplifier?

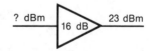

Answer: $L_{Pi} = 23 - 16 = 7 \text{ dBm}$
Check: $7 + 16 = 23$

(See supplementary problem 2-11A.)

Problem 2-13: (a) What is the output voltage level of the following system?

(b) What is the total voltage level gain of the system?

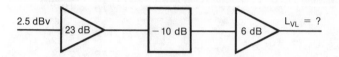

Answer: (a) $L_{VL} = 2.5 + 23 - 10 + 6 = 21.5$ dBv

(b) $L_{VG} = 23 - 10 + 6 = 19$ dB

Problem 2-14: What are the voltage levels at points A, B, and C in this audio chain? The input voltage level is -35 dBv.

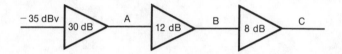

Answer: $L_{VA} = -35 + 30 = -5$ dBv

$L_{VB} = -5 + 12 = 7$ dBv

$L_{VC} = 7 + 8 = 15$ dBv

(See supplementary problems 2-9A and 2-12A.)

Of course, it is not permissible to add decibels to volts or watts, only to dB units such as dBv or dBm. If you must work in decibels and one of the values is given in other units, start by converting the volts or watts to dB units.

Problem 2-15: Find the output voltage level of this amplifier.

$$0.346 \text{ V} \quad \boxed{28 \text{ dB}} \quad ? \text{ dBv}$$

Answer: $.346 \text{ V} = 20 \log \dfrac{.346}{.775}$ dBv

$= -7$ dBv

Therefore,

$L_{VL} = -7 + 28 = 21$ dBv

(See supplementary problems 2-14A and 2-15A.)

Sometimes it is asked, "Why are voltage level gains measured in dB rather than dBv, and power level gains in dB rather than dBm?" The reason is that the level gain refers to the number of decibels above any level, not just above a reference level such as .775 V or 1 mW. The unit dBv, however, specifies the level above the reference voltage (.775 V), and the unit dBm specifies the level above the reference power (1 mW). When level gain is given in dB, the reference level must also be included.

Resistance Level and Level Gain

This section should be treated as a follow-up to the study of decibels. It is suggested that the reader first review the dB formulas and work through the supplementary problems at the end of this chapter, returning to this section only after the concepts of power level and voltage level have been thoroughly understood.

The power at any point in an audio chain is the power absorbed by the load at that point. This depends on two factors— the voltage and the load resistance— and is expressed as V^2/R.

As was mentioned earlier, the power level at any point is numerically equal to the voltage level when the load resistance is the standard value of 600 Ω. A smaller value of load resistance absorbs more power for a given voltage, and a higher value of resistance absorbs less power for the same voltage. Figure 2-3 shows the variation in power level for various loads, the voltage being held constant at 0 dBv.

Fig. 2-3 Variation in power level for loads of various resistances

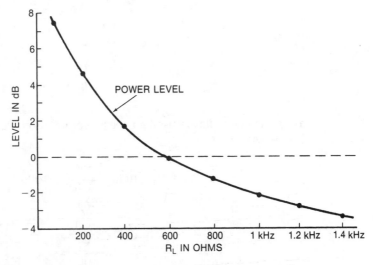

There is thus a difference between the numerical value of L_V and L_P for any load other than 600 Ω. The difference between these levels is called the *resistance level*, and is designated by L_R. It is found from the equation

$$L_R = L_V - L_P \text{ dBr} \qquad (2\text{-}8)$$

In similar fashion, the power level can be found from the equation

$$L_P = L_V - L_R \text{ dBm} \tag{2-9}$$

The resistance level, L_R, is given by

$$L_R = 10 \log \frac{R_L}{R_{ref}}$$

and

$$R_{ref} = 600 \ \Omega \text{ (the standard load resistance)}$$

Therefore,

$$L_R = 10 \log \frac{R_L}{600} \text{ dBr} \tag{2-10}$$

The formula for evaluating L_R is established as follows: Resistance level is defined as the difference between the voltage level and power level, so it is found from Equation 2-8 by definition. However, L_V is numerically equal to the power level produced by this voltage across a 600 Ω load. Therefore,

$$L_V = 10 \log \frac{V^2}{600}$$

and

$$L_P = 10 \log \frac{V^2}{R_L}$$

assuming Mw units are used for the power in both cases. Therefore, Equation 2-8 can be written as

$$L_R = 10 \log \frac{V^2}{600} - 10 \log \frac{V^2}{R_L}$$

$$= 10 \log \frac{\dfrac{V^2}{600}}{\dfrac{V^2}{R_L}}$$

$$= 10 \log \left(\frac{V^2}{600} \times \frac{R_L}{V^2} \right)$$

$$= 10 \log \frac{R_L}{600} \text{ dBr}$$

This illustrates the derivation of Equation 2-10.

To demonstrate a typical application of resistance level, let's consider the following problem. The input resistance of an amplifier is known and its input voltage is known. The requirement is to find the voltage level and power level at this point.

Problem 2-16:   What is the voltage level and power level at an amplifier's input terminal? The input impedance of the amplifier is 2,400 Ω and the input voltage is 5.5 V.

Answer: Voltage level, $L_V = 20 \log \dfrac{5.5}{.775} = 17$ dBv

Next we find L_R.

$$L_R = 10 \log \frac{2400}{600} = 6 \text{ dBr}$$

From Equation 2-9, we see that

$$L_P = L_V - L_R = 17 - 6 = 11 \text{ dBm}$$

As a check, we can find the power level applied to this 2,400 Ω load as follows. First, we calculate the power absorbed by this load when the 5.5 volts are applied.

$$P_L = \frac{V^2}{R_L}$$

$$= \frac{5.5^2}{2400}$$

$$= 12.6 \text{ mW}$$

Then the power level that corresponds to this power is given by

$$L_P = 10 \log \frac{P}{1 \text{ mW}}$$

$$= 10 \log \frac{12.6}{1}$$

$$= 11 \text{ dBm}$$

Just as the term *resistance level* is needed to reconcile the difference between voltage level and power level, so another term called *resistance level gain* is needed to reconcile voltage level gain with power level gain. This need occurs when the two powers develop in load resistances of different values.

As the audio signal travels from point A to point B in an audio chain, the voltage level rises by the amount of the voltage level that has been added. This is called the voltage level gain between points A and B. There will also be a power level gain between these points. Only if the load at point A equals the value of the load resistance at point B will the power level gain equal the voltage level gain. If the load resistances at points A and B are different, the power level gain will not equal the voltage level gain. The difference, which is due to the different values of the load resistances, is called the *resistance level gain*.

In the case of two different voltages being applied to two different resistive loads, such as that at the input and output of an amplifier, the power at these points is given by the following equations:

$$P_i = \frac{V_i^2}{R_i}$$

and

$$P_L = \frac{V_L^2}{R_L}$$

Then the power level difference between them is given by

$$L_{PG} = 10 \log \frac{P_L}{P_i}$$

$$= 10 \log \frac{\frac{V_L^2}{R_L}}{\frac{V_i^2}{R_i}}$$

$$= 10 \log \left(\frac{V_L^2}{R_L} \times \frac{R_i}{V_i^2} \right)$$

$$= 10 \log \left[\left(\frac{V_L}{V_i} \right)^2 \times \frac{R_i}{R_L} \right]$$

$$= 10 \log \left(\frac{V_L}{V_i} \right)^2 + 10 \log \frac{R_i}{R_L}$$

So,

$$L_{PG} = 20 \log \frac{V_L}{V_i} - 10 \log \frac{R_L}{R_i}$$

Inverting the fraction changes the exponent sign. Thus,

$$L_{PG} = L_{VG} - L_{RG} \text{ dB} \tag{2-11}$$

where

$$L_{RG} = 10 \log \frac{R_L}{R_i} \text{ dB} \qquad \text{(2-12)}$$

L_{RG} is called the resistance level gain.

Problem 2-17:   An amplifier with an input resistance of 2,500 Ω is feeding a load of only 500 Ω. The input voltage of the amplifier is 0.976 V. The load voltage is 4.89 V (see Figure 2-4). Find:

(a) The voltage level gain of the amplifier

(b) The power level gain of the amplifier

Fig. 2-4
Schematic
representation of
Problem 2-17

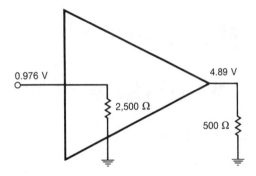

0.976 V

2,500 Ω

4.89 V

500 Ω

Answer: (a) $L_{VG} = 20 \log \dfrac{V_L}{V_i}$

$$= 20 \log \frac{4.89}{.976}$$

$$= 14 \text{ dB}$$

Before we can find the power level gain, it is necessary to find the resistance level gain, and subtract that from the voltage level gain.

$$L_{RG} = 10 \log \frac{R_L}{R_i}$$

$$= 10 \log \frac{500}{2500}$$

$$= -7 \text{ dB}$$

(b) Now it is possible to find the power level gain from

$$L_{PG} = L_{VG} - L_{RG}$$

So,

$$L_{PG} = 14 - (-7) = 21 \text{ dB}$$

To summarize, when the load voltage is anything other than 600 Ω, the power level at that point can be found by subtracting the resistance level from the voltage level. When it is required to find the power level gain between two points at which the load resistances are unequal, the resistance level gain must be subtracted from the voltage level gain to obtain the correct value of power level gain.

Summary of dB Formulas

$$L_P = 10 \log \frac{P}{1 \text{ mW}} \text{ dBm}$$

$$L_V = 20 \log \frac{V}{.775} \text{ dBv}$$

$$L_{PG} = 10 \log \frac{P_L}{P_i} \text{ dB}$$

$$L_{VG} = 20 \log \frac{V_L}{V_i} \text{ dB}$$

$$L_{PG} = L_{PL} - L_{Pi} \text{ dB}$$

$$L_{VG} = L_{VL} - L_{Vi} \text{ dB}$$

$$P \text{ (in watts)} = .001 \times 10^{\frac{L_P}{10}}$$

$$V \text{ (in volts)} = .775 \times 10^{\frac{L_V}{20}}$$

$$G_P = \frac{P_L}{P_i} = 10^{\frac{L_P}{10}}$$

$$G_V = \frac{V_L}{V_i} = 10^{\frac{L_{VG}}{20}}$$

$$L_P = L_V - L_R \quad \text{where} \quad L_R = 10 \log \frac{R_L}{600} \text{ dBr}$$

$$L_{PG} = L_{VG} - L_{RG} \quad \text{where} \quad L_{RG} = 10 \log \frac{R_L}{R_i} \text{ dB}$$

Supplementary Problems and Answers

(Answers to alternate parts of each supplementary problem are given at the end of this section.)

Problems

2-1A. Convert the following to power levels:
    (a) 3.5 W   (b) 186 mW
    (c) 120 W   (d) 0.43 mW

2-2A. What are the power level gains of the following amplifiers?

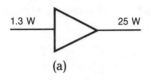

(a)

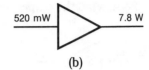

(b)

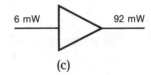

(c)

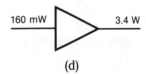

(d)

2-3A. What are the voltage level gains of the following amplifiers?

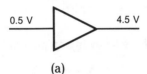

(a)

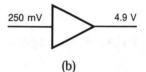

(b)

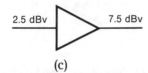

(c)

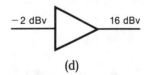

(d)

2-4A. Convert the following to voltage levels:
    (a) 4.5 V   (b) 120 V
    (c) 0.083 V   (d) 77.5 mV

2-5A. Find the power in watts that corresponds to:
    (a) 25 dBm   (b) 7.4 dBm
    (c) −8 dBm   (d) 0 dBm

2-6A. Find the power gain that corresponds to a power level gain of:
    (a) 22 dB   (b) 6 dB
    (c) 10 dB   (d) −3 dB

2-7A. Find the voltage that corresponds to:

(a) 35 dBv   (b) 14 dBv

(c) 0 dBv   (d) – 12 dBv

2-8A. Find the voltage gain of an amplifier that has a voltage level gain of:

(a) 7 dB   (b) 20 dB

(c) 26 dB   (d) – 6 dB

(e) 0 dB

2-9A. Find the output power level of the following amplifiers:

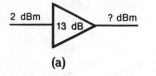   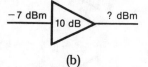

(a)   (b)

2-10A. Find the voltage level gain of the following amplifiers:

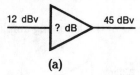   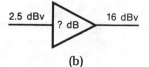

(a)   (b)

2-11A. Find the input power level of the following amplifiers:

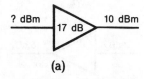   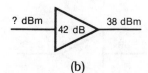

(a)   (b)

2-12A. Find the output voltage level of the following audio chains:

(a)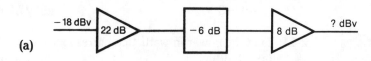

(b)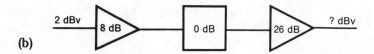

2-13A. **Find the output power** level of the following amplifiers:

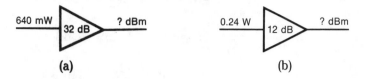

(a)   (b)

2-14A. **Find the** input voltage level of the following amplifiers:

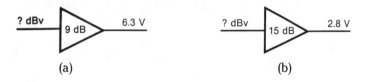

(a)   (b)

2-15A. Find the input and output voltage levels of the following audio chains:

(a)

(b)

Answers

2-1A. (b) $$L_P = 10 \log \frac{186}{1} = 22.7 \text{ dBm}$$

(d) $$L_P = 10 \log \frac{0.43}{1} = -3.7 \text{ dBm}$$

2-2A. (b) $$L_{PG} = 10 \log \frac{7.8}{0.520} = 11.8 \text{ dB}$$

(d) $$L_{PG} = 10 \log \frac{3.4}{0.160} = 13.3 \text{ dB}$$

2-3A. (b) $\qquad L_{VG} = 20 \log \dfrac{4.9}{.250} = 25.8 \text{ dB}$

(d) $\qquad L_{VG} = 16 - (-2) = 18 \text{ dB}$

2-4A. (b) $\qquad L_V = 20 \log \dfrac{120}{.775} = 44 \text{ dBv}$

(d) $\qquad L_V = 20 \log \dfrac{0.0775}{0.775} = -20 \text{ dBv}$

2-5A. (b) $\qquad P = .001 \times 10^{\frac{7.4}{10}} = 5.50 \text{ mW}$

(d) $\qquad P = .001 \times 10^{\frac{0}{10}} = 1 \text{ mW}$

2-6A. (b) $\qquad G_P = 10^{\frac{6}{10}} = 4$

(d) $\qquad G_P = 10^{\frac{-3}{10}} = 0.5$

2-7A. (b) $\qquad V = .775 \times 10^{\frac{14}{20}} = 3.88 \text{ V}$

(d) $\qquad V = .775 \times 10^{\frac{-12}{20}} = 0.195 \text{ V}$

2-8A. (b) $\qquad G_V = 10^{\frac{20}{20}} = 10$

(d) $\qquad G_V = 10^{\frac{-6}{20}} = 0.5$

2-9A. (b) $\qquad L_{PL} = -7 + 10 = 3 \text{ dBm}$

2-10A. (b) $\qquad L_{VG} = 16 - 2.5 = 13.5 \text{ dB}$

2-11A. (b) $\qquad L_{Pi} = 38 - 42 = -4 \text{ dBm}$

2-12A. (b) $\qquad L_{VL} = 2 + 8 + 0 + 26 = 36 \text{ dBv}$

2-13A. (b) $\qquad$ $P_i = 0.24 \text{ W}$

so, $\qquad\qquad\qquad L_{Pi} = 10 \log \dfrac{0.24}{.001} \text{ dBm}$

$$L_{Pi} = 23.8 \text{ dBm}$$

0.24 W
12 dB
$L_{Pi} = 23.8 \text{ dBm}$ $\qquad\qquad L_{PL} = 35.8 \text{ dBm}$

$$L_{PL} = 23.8 + 12 = 35.8 \text{ dBm}$$

2-14A. (b) $\qquad\qquad\qquad V_L = 2.8\text{V}$

so, $\qquad\qquad\qquad L_{VL} = 20 \log \dfrac{2.8}{.775}$

$$L_{VL} = 11.2 \text{ dBv}$$

-3.8 dBv
15 dB
2.8 V
$L_{VL} = 11.2 \text{ dBv}$

$$L_{Vi} = 11.2 - 15 = -3.8 \text{ dBv}$$

2-15A. (b) $\qquad$ $15.5 \text{ mV} = \text{A level of } 20 \log \dfrac{.0155}{.775} = -34 \text{ dBv}$

-39 dBv
5 dB
15.5 mV
-34 dBv
9 dB
-25 dBV

$$L_{VL} = -34 + 9 = -25 \text{ dBv}$$
$$L_{Vi} = -34 - 5 = -39 \text{ dBv}$$

3 Operational Amplifiers

3 Operational Amplifiers

Op-Amp Characteristics

Op-amps were originally developed to perform mathematical operations—such as multiplying, dividing, adding, and subtracting data—in the form of analog voltages. The amplification characteristics needed for this purpose turned out to be ideally suitable for the processing of audio and video signals. Consequently, a new field of op-amp applications suddenly opened up, which boosted the economic efficiency and quality of most aspects of electronics. When one considers that a dual op-amp (two amplifiers in an integrated circuit chip about half an inch square) can be obtained for about the cost of a fuse, the imagination boggles.

The amplifier characteristics that enabled these mathematical operations to take place are

- Extremely high open-circuit gain
- Extremely high input impedance
- Extremely low output impedance
- Wide bandwidth (including DC amplification)

In describing these characteristics, when I say "extremely high," I mean the value is so great that we can take the figure as infinitely high for calculation purposes. Audio and video signal processing requires many low-power, high-quality amplifiers such as these. You will see how these characteristics lend themselves to signal processing in the following sections.

Inverting Amplifiers

The schematic symbol for an op-amp consists of a triangular shape (used for all types of amplifiers) with two inputs at the left and a single output on the right (see Figure 3-1). The DC power supply runs vertically, according to normal convention.

Fig. 3-1
Schematic symbol
for an op-amp

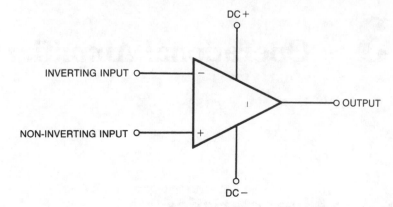

The minus sign at the inverting input does *not* mean that the input is of negative voltage. Nor does this input have anything to do with the power supply. It simply means that this is the inverting input, and that the output will be amplified but of opposite polarity to this input. Thus, a positive input voltage here will produce an amplified negative output. A negative voltage here will produce an amplified positive output. And an AC input here will produce an amplified output 180° out of phase with the input. Similarly, the plus sign at the non-inverting input means that the resulting output will be in phase with this input.

By the addition of only three external resistors, this op-amp can be made into an inverting amplifier having any required gain and input resistance. The schematic for this is shown in Figure 3-2A. (The DC power supply inputs are not shown. It is assumed that they exist.)

Due to extremely high input impedance, no measurable current enters the input terminals. Consequently, there is no measurable current through R_g. Because R_g conducts zero current, there is no voltage drop across it, so the non-inverting input is at the same voltage as ground.

The open circuit gain of the differential amplifier is almost infinitely high. Because a differential amplifier amplifies the voltage difference between the two input terminals, this differential voltage has to be kept extremely small to avoid overloading. In fact, it never exceeds about 1 microvolt (almost immeasurably small), so you can always assume that the two input terminals are at the same voltage. And because the non-inverting input terminal is at ground potential, the inverting input terminal must also be at ground potential (within 1 microvolt). This inverting input terminal is, therefore, said to be at *virtual ground*. This means *ground* for all calculation purposes.

Fig. 3-2
Inverting op-amp

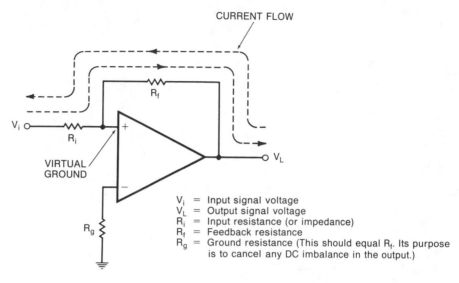

V_i = Input signal voltage
V_L = Output signal voltage
R_i = Input resistance (or impedance)
R_f = Feedback resistance
R_g = Ground resistance (This should equal R_f. Its purpose is to cancel any DC imbalance in the output.)

(A) Schematic

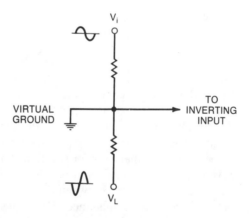

(B) Equivalent circuit

The other consequence of the extremely high input impedance is that no current can flow in or out at the inverting input. In fact, the current flows through R_i and then continues through R_f. During the next half cycle, when the signal voltage is reversed, the current flows in the opposite direction, back through R_f and then back through R_i. In effect, R_i and R_f form two resistors in series with each other; so the equivalent circuit looks like that shown in Figure 3-2B. During the first half of a cycle, if V_i is positive, V_L is negative, and conventional current flows downward from V_i to V_L. In the second half of the cycle, when the potentials are reversed, current flow is upward. Because the current is the same in all parts of a series circuit, it can be stated that

$$I_i = I_f$$

where
  I_i = Current in R_i
  I_f = Current in R_f

By Ohm's Law,

$$\frac{V_i}{R_i} = \frac{V_L}{R_f}$$

From this equation, we arrive at

$$\frac{V_L}{V_i} = \frac{R_f}{R_i}$$

But by definition,

$$\frac{V_L}{V_i} = \text{Voltage gain, } G_V$$

Therefore,

$$G_V = \frac{R_f}{R_i}$$

Thus, the voltage gain of an inverting op-amp is controlled entirely by the resistance ratio between R_f and R_i.

In addition to being able to determine the voltage gain of an op-amp, the input impedance can also be predetermined. The input impedance, as you know, is the effective impedance (or resistance) between the input terminal and ground. However, the inverting input of this amplifier is at *virtual ground*. Because R_i is the effective resistance between the input of the circuit and this virtual ground, R_i acts as the input impedance. Consequently, you can choose whatever input impedance you desire simply by making R_i that value. It is easy, therefore, to construct an op-amp of any required input impedance and gain, as shown in Problem 3-1.

Problem 3-1:   It is required to make a pre-amplifier with a voltage gain of 50 and an input impedance of 8 kΩ.

Answer: R_i is fixed at 8 kΩ by the input impedance requirement. Because

$$G_V = \frac{R_f}{R_i}$$

then

$$R_f = G_V R_i$$

and

$$R_f = 50 \times 8000$$
$$= 400 \text{ k}\Omega$$

The final circuit is shown in Figure 3-3.

Fig. 3-3
Pre-amplifier with
voltage gain of 50
and input
impedance of
8 kΩ

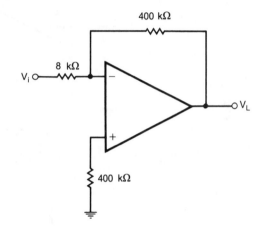

Non-inverting Amplifiers

By applying the incoming signal to the non-inverting input, a non-inverting amplifier can be made. This circuit is illustrated in Figure 3-4A. In this type of amplifier, the non-inverting input is not held at ground potential as was the case with the inverting amplifier. In addition, there is no virtual ground. In fact, both inputs (and the whole amplifier) are at the AC voltage of the incoming signal, oscillating with the amplitude and frequency of the signal. This can be seen from the equivalent circuit shown in Figure 3-4B.

Again, the current flows through R_i and R_f in series. Because the amplifier is non-inverting, the input signal is in phase with the output. So both signal voltages are positive together or negative together. The gain of this amplifier can be found by considering the equivalent circuit shown in Figure 3-4B. The current being the same in all parts of a series circuit,

$$I_i = I_T$$

where
I_i = Current in R_i
I_T = Total circuit current

Fig. 3-4
Non-inverting
op-amp

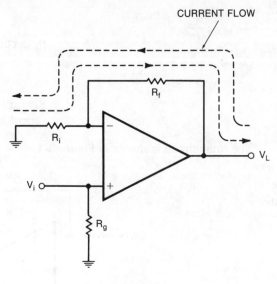

(A) Schematic

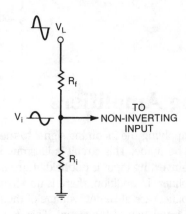

(B) Equivalent circuit

Writing I as $\dfrac{V}{R}$, the above equation becomes

$$\frac{V_i}{R_i} = \frac{V_L}{R_i + R_f}$$

So,

$$\frac{V_L}{V_i} = \frac{R_i + R_f}{R_i}$$

or,

$$\frac{V_L}{V_i} = 1 + \frac{R_f}{R_i}$$

However,

$$\frac{V_L}{V_i} = \text{Gain, } G_V$$

So the gain of a non-inverting op-amp can be found from

$$G_V = 1 + \frac{R_f}{R_i}$$

As in the previous amplifier, both gain and input impedance are determined by the external resistance values. Because the input impedance is the effective resistance between the incoming signal and ground, and because the incoming signal voltage occurs at both the inverting and non-inverting inputs, it follows that the input impedance is made up of the two resistors R_i and R_g in parallel. (If the gain is high, R_g is large compared with R_i, so the input resistance approximates R_i.) In general, the input impedance of a non-inverting op-amp can be found from

$$Z_i = \frac{R_i R_g}{R_i + R_g}$$

Note that the gain of a non-inverting op-amp can never be less than unity. So this amplifier configuration can only amplify and never attenuate, whereas an inverting op-amp can both amplify and attenuate a signal.

Stepped Gain Amplifiers

Because the gain of an inverting op-amp can be entirely determined by the ratio of the two resistors (R_f/R_i) and because this amplifier can both amplify and attenuate, an inverting op-amp is often used where stepped gain amplification is required—for example, in situations such as the vertical input of an oscilloscope or the range control of a VTVM. In both of these situations, it is required to alter the voltage gain at the input terminal by predetermined steps, as opposed to the continuously variable requirement needed by a volume control.

Take as an example the vertical input of an oscilloscope. The vertical amplifier of this equipment is designed to supply a voltage to the vertical deflection plates of the cathode ray tube, which causes the trace to move up or down, depending on the applied input voltage. Suppose this vertical amplifier were calibrated to produce a sensitivity of 0.01 V per centimeter deflection. In this case, an acceptable trace would appear from input voltages between − .05 V and + .05 V. (Each would produce a 5 cm deflection either upward or downward.)

But suppose the input voltages were very small, in the region of 5 mV. Then the deflection would be hardly visible. In this case, a range control switch would be needed. When set to the 1 mV range, it would amplify the input by 10, thus converting the 5 mV input to .05 V at the input of the vertical amplifier, and producing an acceptable trace of 5 cm deflection. Similarly, if the input voltage happened to be large, in the region of 500 V, the range control would have to attenuate this down to .05 V, or most of the trace would be lost above and below the screen.

Assume that the sensitivity of the vertical amplifier produces a deflection of 1 cm for an input of .01 V, its sensitivity being .01 V/cm (or 10 mV/cm). Assume also that the required input ranges are 1 mV, 10 mV, 100 mV, 1 V, 10 V, and 100 V each per centimeter. This could be achieved quite simply. The required gains would be, from the lowest to the highest, 10, 1, .1, .01, .001, and .0001. The low input voltage obviously requires gain, and the high input voltage requires attenuation. Now assume that the input impedance of this oscilloscope has to be high, say 2 MΩ. This would be the value of R_i in our stepped gain inverting op-amp. Then the required circuit resistances could be found in the following way:

$$G_V = \frac{R_f}{R_i}$$

So,

$$R_f = R_i \, G_V$$

But R_i is already determined by the input impedance requirement of 2 MΩ.
So,

$$R_f = 2 \text{ M}\Omega \times G_V$$

For each gain listed, it is therefore possible to calculate the required feedback resistor from this formula simply by multiplying the gain by 2 MΩ. The resulting range setting, required gain, and feedback resistors are listed in Table 3-1. The first value of R_f is given by

$$R_f = 2 \text{ M}\Omega \times 10 = 20 \text{ M}\Omega$$

The schematic of a stepped gain op-amp that could be used in this situation is shown in Figure 3-5. It can be seen that as the moving contact of the switch is connected to the various feedback resistors, the gain is changed in discrete steps. At each setting, the gain consists of the actual value of R_f/R_i. R_i is constant. The six different values of R_f produce the required six different gains needed for the various input range settings.

Table 3-1
Feedback resistors needed for vertical sensitivity control of an oscilloscope

Input Range	Required Gain	Feedback Resistance
1 mV	10	20 MΩ
10 mV	1	2 MΩ
100 mV	.1	200 kΩ
1 V	.01	20 kΩ
10 V	.001	2 kΩ
100 V	.0001	200 Ω

Fig. 3-5 Stepped gain op-amp

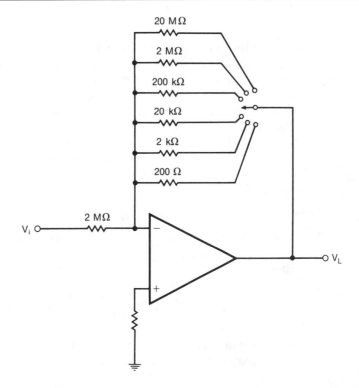

Summing Amplifiers

One of the situations where the audio and video application of op-amps is most often used is in the *summing amplifier*. This forms the basic mixer circuit. It is particularly advantageous because at the inverting input (which is used as the summing point), the voltage is at virtual ground. Consequently, there is no feedback to other channels. The summing amplifier circuit is shown in Figure 3-6.

Fig. 3-6
Summing op-amp

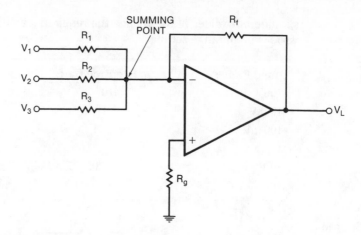

The theoretical basis for the summing action of this amplifier can be seen by application of Kirchhoff's Current Law. Kirchhoff states that at any point in a circuit, the total current entering equals the total current leaving. Applying this principle to the summing point in Figure 3-6, the current entering this point is through the input resistors R_1, R_2, and R_3. All current leaving travels through R_f. Therefore,

$$I_1 + I_2 + I_3 = I_f$$

By Ohm's Law,

$$\frac{V_1}{R_1} + \frac{V_2}{R_2} + \frac{V_3}{R_3} = \frac{V_L}{R_f}$$

Thus,

$$V_L = V_1 \left(\frac{R_f}{R_1}\right) + V_2 \left(\frac{R_f}{R_2}\right) + V_3 \left(\frac{R_f}{R_3}\right)$$

For purely mathematical summing, the input resistors are all of the same value. Call this value R_i. Then the equation becomes

$$V_L = V_1 \left(\frac{R_f}{R_i}\right) + V_2 \left(\frac{R_f}{R_i}\right) + V_3 \left(\frac{R_f}{R_i}\right)$$

Factoring, this produces the following equation:

$$V_L = \frac{R_f}{R_i}(V_1 + V_2 + V_3) \tag{3-1}$$

This illustrates the summing function. Of course, any number of inputs can be faders. A typical four-input mixer circuit is shown in Figure 3-7. R_1 through R_4 are input faders. R_m is the master gain. R_f is the feedback resistor. And R_i is the value of the input resistors needed to limit the gain to the required maximum level.

Fig. 3-7 Mixer circuit

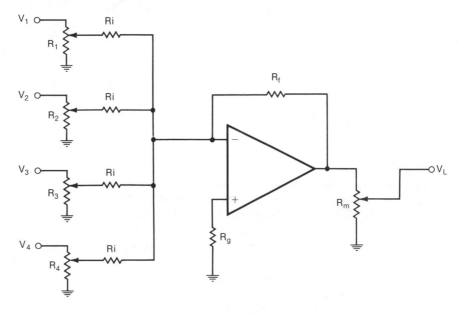

Differential Amplifiers

The fact that the op-amp has an inverting and a non-inverting input characterizes it as a differential amplifier. This means that it must amplify the voltage differential between the two inputs. For example, suppose the gain for both inputs were 5. An input of $+1$ V at the inverting input would then produce an output of -5 V. A similar input of $+1$ V at the non-inverting input would produce an output of $+5$ V. These two outputs, namely -5 V and $+5$ V, would cancel each other out. So it is clear that an identical voltage at both inputs produces no output voltage. Only a *difference* between input voltages produces any output.

In the case of an op-amp, its extremely high open-circuit gain necessitates a reduction in gain by means of negative feedback. If this is not done, the amplifier will become unstable and give out a continuous howl. Thus, the basic differential amplifier circuit looks like that in Figure 3-8.

If this amplifier is designed to give equal weight to both inputs, the two input resistors R_i should be of equal value. For optimum DC balance, R_g should equal R_f. Then the resulting output voltage will be given by

$$V_L = \frac{R_f}{R_i} (V_2 - V_1) \tag{3-2}$$

Fig. 3-8
Differential
amplifier

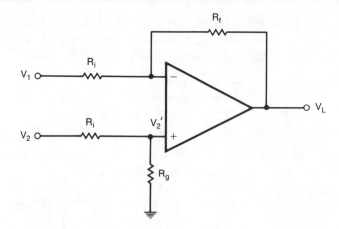

Because R_f/R_i represents the gain factor, it can be seen that the output voltage is equal to the gain times the *difference* between the input voltages. This illustrates the amplifier's differential characteristic. The mathematical derivation of Equation 3-2 is given in the appendix at the end of this book.

The differential amplifier has many useful applications. Perhaps one of the most useful is its ability to filter noise from a balanced line input. Low-level signals, such microphone signals, are most susceptible to noise. This is because noise voltages are at nearly the same level as the mic signal. The audio signal being fed to a loudspeaker is normally in the range of 5 to 10 volts; a noise voltage of 7 millivolts represents a negligible proportion of this signal. However, 7 millivolts of noise will cause a disastrous amount of interference with a 15 mV microphone signal.

An unbalanced line uses two conductors. The balanced line system uses three conductors. One carries the ground of 0 volts. The other two conductors carry opposing polarities equally balanced on each side of ground potential. Figure 3-9 illustrates the difference between an unbalanced and a balanced line. Note that both carry the same signal. The two balanced conductors each carry half of the waveform amplitude. These add across the differential input terminals to give a full waveform input.

Let us assume that a microphone line is receiving noise interference in the form of low-frequency hum. The required signal and noise can be graphed individually as shown in Figure 3-10A and B. When combined in an unbalanced line and passed through a non-inverting amplifier, the results are as shown in Figure 3-10C. Note that the signal and noise have both been amplified equally. If this same microphone signal were carried by a balanced line (which is achieved by keeping the ground conductor separate from either of the signal conductors) and if the amplifier were a differential amplifier, then the waveforms would appear as in Figure 3-10D.

You can see that the low-frequency noise is in phase in both conductors, so it produces no differential voltage across the input terminals. Therefore, it produces no output voltage. Only the required signal (opposite in phase on each conductor)

Fig. 3-9 Signal voltages applied to an unbalanced and a balanced line

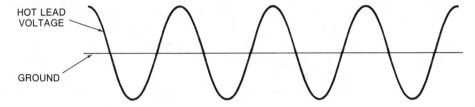

HOT LEAD VOLTAGE

GROUND

(A) Unbalanced line (using two conductors)

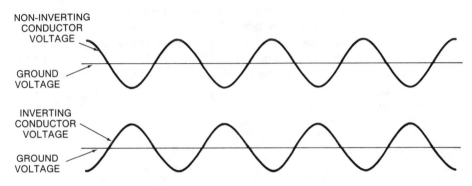

NON-INVERTING CONDUCTOR VOLTAGE

GROUND VOLTAGE

INVERTING CONDUCTOR VOLTAGE

GROUND VOLTAGE

(B) Balanced line (using three conductors)

Fig. 3-10 Noise amplification vs. noise filtering

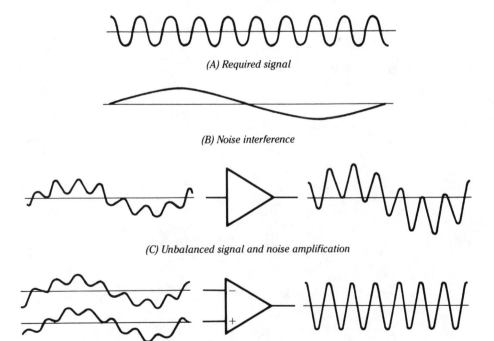

(A) Required signal

(B) Noise interference

(C) Unbalanced signal and noise amplification

(D) Balanced line—signal amplification and noise elimination

has been amplified. This demonstrates one of the great advantages that can be obtained from a differential amplifier. It is called *common mode rejection*, and amounts to a useful ability to eliminate noise interference.

Comparatively few of the many applications of op-amps have been discussed so far. This is because it is necessary first to clarify the principle characteristics of op-amps. In fact, op-amps are used in audio and video technology for many aspects of signal processing. For instance, they are used as pre-amplifiers, line amplifiers, mixers, equalizers, compressors, expanders, active filters, tone controls, analog comparators and buffers in digital systems, digital-to-analog converters, and so forth. The list goes on and on. Some of these applications will be mentioned later. At this stage, it is only necessary to understand the fundamentals of op-amp characteristics and behavior. Once this has been understood, it is then possible to troubleshoot or construct audio components with awareness of the principles behind their applications.

4 Passive Filters

4 Passive Filters

Filtering Concepts

The action of a filter is to exclude certain objects or characteristics, while allowing others to pass. In the realm of electronics, a filter discriminates between frequencies. A low-pass filter passes the low frequencies, while it filters out the high. A high-pass filter does the reverse. With a little ingenuity, more sophisticated filters can be made that filter out one band of frequencies or allow only a limited band to pass. Others, called active filters, can not only attenuate, but also amplify. A tone control or equalizer is of this nature.

However, there is an altogether different group of filters that have to be dealt with by the audio engineer. These are the ones that we don't want, but can't avoid. They are the troublemakers. And it is the need to be able to deal with these that requires us to understand something about the theory of filtering.

Unintentional filters can result from such things as the reactance of the coil in a magnetic tape head or the capacitance in a long microphone cable. They can destroy the quality of a recording or sound reinforcement system by cutting out frequencies that should be present. It is important to be able to counteract the effect of these filters or at least to confine it to a range of frequencies where it will be harmless.

All filtering results from the action of reactive components such as inductors (coils) or capacitors. The reactance of these components to AC voltages is frequency dependent. This means that their opposition to current varies, depending on its frequency. Remember that capacitive reactance (a capacitor's opposition to current) is inversely proportional to frequency. The higher the frequency, the less the capacitor opposes current, in accordance with the formula,

$$X_c = \frac{1}{2\pi fC}$$

The reactance of an inductor, on the other hand, is exactly opposite, as given by the formula,

$$X_L = 2\pi fL$$

This means that the higher the frequency, the more it opposes current. These two facts hold the whole key to filtering theory, so they are important to remember.

- A capacitor passes high frequencies, but blocks low.
- An inductor passes low frequencies, but blocks high.

With this knowledge, it is possible to look at any filtering circuit and tell instantly what sort of filter it is and what it is likely to do at different frequencies. Of course, it requires mathematical analysis to pinpoint the quantitative effect. But it is easy to obtain a general picture, and that is helpful.

Both a capacitor and an inductor can be used in conjunction to produce an increased filtering effect. However, at a certain frequency, when both of their reactances are numerically equal, they will go into electronic resonance. This can be used under certain circumstances—for example, to achieve a tuned circuit—because at their resonant frequency they can greatly amplify an applied signal. This is how a radio or TV is tuned. But they do not form what is called a precision filter, such as a low- or high-pass filter, in which the effect is linearly proportional to frequency. And this is what is required for a bass and treble tone control.

In fact, a precision filter can be made out of a single reactive component, either a capacitor or an inductor in conjunction with resistors. The reactive component chosen is almost always a capacitor. Hence, precision audio filters are mostly RC filters containing only resistors and capacitors. The reason why capacitors are chosen is two-fold. First, they are cheaper than inductors. But more important, an inductor progressively becomes less efficient as frequency drops, due to the fact that the resistance of the winding becomes more significant than the reactance of the coil at lower frequencies. Having said this, we will now ignore any imperfections in filtering components and look at the theoretical basis of filtering. This is best seen by examination of simple low-pass and high-pass circuits.

Most RC filters can be thought of as forming a voltage divider made up of two impedances, Z_1 and Z_2 (see Figure 4-1). The output (filtered) voltage is that which develops across Z_2. The ratio of output voltage to input (source) voltage, V_o/V_i, is called the *transfer function*, designated by the letters H(f). The voltage gain, G_V, of an amplifier is also the ratio V_o/V_i. The difference is that the transfer function is frequency dependent, whereas the gain of an amplifier is constant at all frequencies.

- Amplifier gain is given by

$$G_V = \frac{V_o}{V_i}$$

- Transfer function is given by

$$H(f) = \frac{V_o}{V_i}$$

The suffix (f) indicates that the value of H is a function of f, the frequency. That means it will be different at different frequencies.

Fig. 4-1 Voltage divider

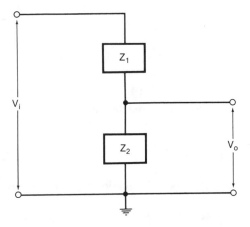

In a voltage divider, as in Figure 4-1, the ratio of the voltages is equal to the ratio of the impedances. (This results from the Voltage Proportionality Law.) So the transfer function, from Figure 4-1, is given by

$$H(f) = \frac{V_o}{V_i} = \frac{Z_2}{\overrightarrow{Z_1 + Z_2}}$$

The half arrow over $Z_1 + Z_2$ means that these two impedances must be added vectorially, taking their magnitude and phase (relative direction) into account. Because they are at right angles in an RC circuit, they cannot be added algebraically.

To simplify any phase angle problems, we will use the complex frequency variable *S* when calculating capacitive reactance. This takes phase angle into account automatically and solves all phase related problems. In this way, the phase angle will be included in the frequency terms. *S* is defined as follows:

$$S = j\omega$$

where

    S = Complex frequency variable
    j = The imaginary number ($= \sqrt{-1}$), indicating change of dimension or
        phase angle of $+90°$
    ω = Radial frequency, the number of radians turned per second ($= 2\pi f$,
        where f is the number of cycles per second)

So, the radial frequency phasor *S* is given by

$$S = j\omega$$

But,

$$\omega = 2\pi f$$

So,

$$S = j2\pi f$$

Now, capacitive reactance is given by

$$X_c = \frac{-j}{2\pi fC}$$

(being in the $-j$ direction with respect to resistance).
So,

$$X_c = \frac{1}{j2\pi fC} \qquad\qquad \text{(because } -j = 1/j\text{)}.$$

But,

$$j2\pi f = S$$

So,

$$X_c = \frac{1}{SC}$$

We will use $1/SC$ for X_c in future, to simplify all calculations.

Low-Pass Passive Filters

A single element LP (low-pass) or HP (high-pass) filter is made up of a single resistor and capacitor forming a voltage divider. It is possible to visualize the action of these filters by remembering that capacitive reactance increases as frequency falls, and that voltage across the capacitor follows the capacitive reactance. Thus, Figure 4-2A represents an LP filter, because its output voltage increases at low frequencies. Similarly, Figure 4-2B represents an HP filter, because the voltage lost across the capacitor falls as frequency rises. This leaves more voltage across the resistor at high frequencies.

Fig. 4-2 Single element filters

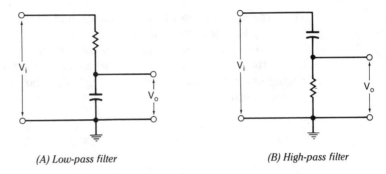

(A) Low-pass filter   *(B) High-pass filter*

The transfer function of the LP filter is given by

$$H(S) = \frac{V_o}{V_i} = \frac{X_c}{R + X_c} = \frac{1/SC}{R + (1/SC)}$$

Multiplying numerator and denominator by SC,

$$H(S) = \frac{1}{SRC + 1} \qquad (4\text{-}1)$$

But in an RC series circuit, the time constant, designated by the Greek letter T (pronounced Tau) is given by

$$T = RC$$

Substituting this in Equation 4-1, the standard form for the transfer function of an LP filter becomes

$$H(S) = \frac{1}{ST + 1} \qquad (4\text{-}2)$$

It is useful to note that the term $(ST + 1)$ is the mathematical representation of all single element filters. It demonstrates that the time constant of the circuit is the key element in determining the frequency at which it takes effect. But more about this later.

From the standard form of an LP filter, namely H(S) = 1/(ST + 1), it can be seen that at very low frequencies, when the radial frequency S is very low, the term ST becomes negligible. Then the transfer function becomes

$$H(0) = \frac{1}{0+1} = \frac{1}{1} = 1$$

Thus, there is no loss of signal voltage and the graph of output plotted on a frequency base is a horizontal line.

However, when we consider the high-frequency response, when S is very large, the term ST becomes so large compared with the added 1 in the denominator that the 1 becomes negligible. So the high-frequency transfer function becomes

$$H(\infty) = \frac{1}{S T + 0} = \frac{1}{S T}$$

This represents a graph in which the value is inversely proportional to frequency. If S doubles, 1/ST halves, and so on. The low- and high-frequency responses of this filter, as a level change (in dB units), are illustrated in Figure 4-3.

Fig. 4-3 Limiting response of an LP filter

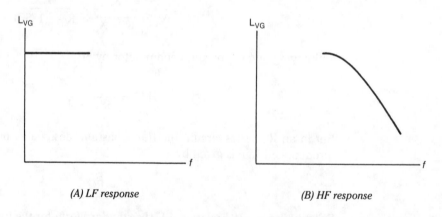

(A) LF response   (B) HF response

Of course, the actual filter response doesn't suddenly change from a perfectly straight horizontal line to a straight downward sloping line. At intermediate frequencies, there is a curve joining these two limiting responses. However, the two lines illustrated in Figure 4-3 show exactly what happens at the low- and high-frequency limits. They also form what are called *asymptotes*. An asymptote is a straight line which a curve ever more closely approaches, but never quite reaches. Asymptotes are useful because they form a graphical structure within which the filter curve fits. The downward slope can be found from the fact that the output voltage halves its value at each higher octave (double the frequency). The corresponding voltage level change per octave (since the voltage ratio is ½) is given by

$$L_{VG} = 20 \log \tfrac{1}{2}$$
$$= 20 \times (-.3)$$
$$= -6 \text{ dB/octave}$$

It is of fundamental significance that the output of this filter tends to a -6 dB/octave slope as the frequency rises. But this is only valid at high frequencies. At low frequencies, the graph becomes a horizontal line.

The next, and equally important, characteristic of this filter is the frequency at which the transition occurs between the horizontal and sloping lines. This can be found by extending the two lines until they meet in a corner. At that point, the filter is said to *break*, so this is called the *break frequency*, or *corner frequency*. Filters with different value components can be made to break at different frequencies. Another way to look at it is this: It is only when the frequency has risen to a high enough level to reduce X_c to a value comparable to that of R, in the filter circuit, that filtering takes place. In fact, this frequency, the break frequency, is specified as occurring when X_c is numerically equal to R. Then,

$$R = X_c = \frac{1}{S_1 C}$$

(S_1 being the frequency at which this equality occurs). And so,

$$S_1 = \frac{1}{RC}$$

RC is the time constant of an RC series circuit, namely T. So,

$$S_1 = \frac{1}{T_1}$$

But in general, S is numerically equal to $2\pi f$. Thus,

$$2\pi f_1 = \frac{1}{T_1}$$

Therefore,

$$f_1 = \frac{1}{2\pi T_1} \tag{4-3}$$

where
    f_1 = Break frequency in hertz
    T_1 = Time constant of the circuit in seconds

The break frequency is found from the circuit time constant, and the circuit time constant from the appropriate combination of the circuit component values. Thus, analyzing filtering circuits simplifies itself into finding the time constants of the filtering elements. From each time constant we can find the corresponding break frequency from

$$f_1 = \frac{1}{2\pi T_1}, \qquad f_2 = \frac{1}{2\pi T_2}, \qquad \text{etc.}$$

There is a problem in evaluating the transfer function of a filter at any frequency f, because the frequency variable in our standard form is a complex frequency term. As stated earlier, $S = j\omega$. Also, the time constant is defined as the period that corresponds to the radial frequency at which $R = X_c$. Therefore,

$$T_1 = \frac{1}{\omega_1}$$

Substituting these identities—$S = j\omega$ and $T_1 = 1/\omega_1$—we obtain

$$(ST_1 + 1) = \frac{j\omega}{\omega_1} + 1$$

Because the j term is at right angles to the number term, we can evaluate by Pythagoras' theorem. Or, we can convert from rectangular form to polar form, as follows:

$$(ST_1 + 1) = \sqrt{\left(\frac{\omega}{\omega_1}\right)^2 + 1}$$

It is more convenient to use cyclical rather than radial frequencies; however, the frequency ratios are interchangeable, the 2π conversion factors canceling out. Thus,

$$(ST_1 + 1) = \sqrt{\left(\frac{f}{f_1}\right)^2 + 1}$$

where

f = A given frequency in Hz
f_1 = Break frequency in Hz

Any filtering term can, therefore, be evaluated by converting each $(ST_n + 1)$ term to

$$\sqrt{\left(\frac{f}{f_n}\right)^2 + 1}$$

It is often more convenient to find the effect of a filter in terms of voltage level change, rather than as voltage gain. This can easily be achieved because H(f) is a voltage ratio; therefore, the corresponding level gain is given by

$$L_{VG} = 20 \log H(f) \qquad (4\text{-}4)$$

Our LP filter transfer function from Equation 4-2 can now be written as a level change.

$$(4\text{-}5)$$

$$L_{VG} = 20 \log \frac{1}{\sqrt{\left(\frac{f}{f_1}\right)^2 + 1}} \text{ dB}$$

As mentioned earlier, between the horizontal asymptote in Figure 4-3 and the sloping asymptote, there is a curve that bridges the transition. Thus, the level at break frequency will be somewhat below its maximum value. To find out how much this level will drop, we use Equation 4-5 to evaluate the level change *at* break frequency. At this frequency, f is specified as equal to f_1, the break frequency. Then, Equation 4-5 becomes

$$L_{VG} = 20 \log \frac{1}{\sqrt{\left(\frac{f_1}{f_1}\right)^2 + 1}}$$

$$= 20 \log \frac{1}{\sqrt{2}}$$

$$= 20 \times (-0.1505)$$

$$= -3 \text{ dB}$$

This 3 dB drop at break frequency is characteristic of all single element filters.

It is now possible to plot the output response level of a single element LP filter, and compare the actual response with the LF and HF asymptotes (see Figure 4-4). The vertical axis is the voltage level gain. The frequency base is scaled in octaves. This is logarithmic base 2, so each equal increment (representing one octave increase) is twice the frequency of the previous increment.

Notice that the point at which the horizontal and sloping lines meet identifies the break frequency. The 3 dB down level has special significance. It is conventionally taken as the *cutoff point*. By this I mean that any signal that has fallen by 3 dB or more is said to have been cut off. (While -3 dB is not all that much of an attenuation, the line has to be drawn somewhere, and this is where it

Fig. 4-4 Typical
LP filter response

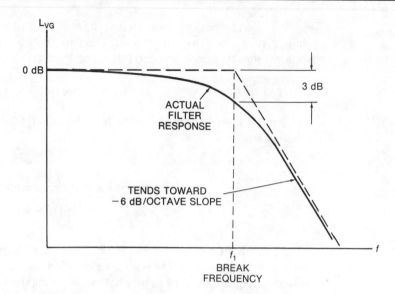

is drawn.) So, in audio technology, output signals at 3 dB or more below the maximum value are said to have been cut off. In this LP filter, all frequencies above the break frequency are cut off. In this type of filter, the break frequency is often called the *cutoff frequency* or, as noted previously, the *corner frequency*.

It is now possible to calculate the response of an actual filter at various frequencies, as shown in Problem 4-1.

Problem 4-1:   In the filter circuit shown in Figure 4-5, find:

(a) The break frequency

(b) The response level at break frequency

(c) The response level at 23 kHz

Fig. 4-5 Filtering
circuit specified in
Problem 4-1

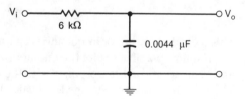

Answer: (a) To find the break frequency, use Equation 4-3.

$$f_1 = \frac{1}{2\pi T_1}$$

In an RC series circuit,

$$T_1 = RC$$

From these component values,

$$T_1 = (6 \times 10^3) \times (0.0044 \times 10^{-6}) = 24 \ \mu sec$$

So,

$$f_1 = \frac{1}{2\pi \times 24 \times 10^{-6}}$$

Thus, the break frequency is given by

$$f_1 = 6.63 \ kHz$$

(b) **To find the response** level at break frequency (when f = 6.63 kHz), use Equation 4-5.

$$L_{VG} = 20 \log \frac{1}{\sqrt{\left(\frac{6.63}{6.63}\right)^2 + 1}}$$

$$= 20 \log \frac{1}{\sqrt{2}}$$

$$= -3 \ dB$$

(c) To find the response level at 23 kHz, use Equation 4-5 again.

$$L_{VG} = 20 \log \frac{1}{\sqrt{\left(\frac{23}{6.63}\right)^2 + 1}}$$

$$= -11.15 \ dB$$

Summary of RC Low-Pass Filter Characteristics

1. The break frequency (above which the filtering action becomes apparent) is inversely proportional to the time constant, which equals the product of RC. It is given by

$$f_1 = \frac{1}{2\pi T_1}$$

or

$$f_1 = \frac{1}{2\pi RC}$$

where

f_1 = Break frequency in Hz
R = Resistance in ohms
C = Capacitance in farads
τ_1 = Time constant in seconds

2. At break frequency, the level is 3 dB below its maximum value. All frequencies above this are cut off.

3. At high frequencies, the filter's response falls off at a rate approaching -6 dB/octave.

High-Pass Passive Filters

An HP filter circuit is shown in Figure 4-6. To understand how this circuit passes high frequencies while filtering out low, it is only necessary to remember that, at very high frequencies, the capacitive reactance becomes extremely small; therefore, the capacitor acts as a shorting link, then all input voltage passes to the output. At very low frequencies, the capacitive reactance becomes very large, much larger than the resistor; therefore, the majority of the voltage is lost across the capacitor. Only the small portion that develops across the resistor reaches the output. It can, therefore, be seen that this filter passes the high frequencies and filters out the low.

Fig. 4-6 HP passive filter

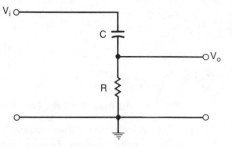

The transfer function, by definition, is equal to the voltage ratio, V_o/V_i. This, in turn, is equal to the impedence ratio, which is given by

$$H(S) = \frac{R}{\frac{1}{SC} + R}$$

Multiplying numerator and denominator by SC,

$$H(S) = \frac{SRC}{1 + SRC}$$

But, in an RC series circuit, $RC = T$; therefore,

$$H(S) = \frac{ST}{1 + ST} \tag{4-6}$$

This is the standard form for an HP filter transfer function. For calculation purposes it is convenient to divide the numerator and denominator by ST. Then,

$$H(S) = \frac{1}{\dfrac{1}{ST} + 1}$$

As we did before, we can substitute $j\omega$ for S, and ω_1 for $1/T_1$. The function then becomes

$$H(\omega) = \frac{1}{\dfrac{\omega_1}{j\omega} + 1}$$

We then convert from rectangular form to polar form, to obtain the numerical value.

$$H(\omega) = \frac{1}{\sqrt{\left(\dfrac{\omega_1}{\omega}\right)^2 + 1}}$$

Replacing the radial frequency ratio with the cyclical frequency ratio,

$$H(f) = \frac{1}{\sqrt{\left(\dfrac{f_1}{f}\right)^2 + 1}}$$

gives a method for calculating the transfer function at any frequency, *f*. As a level change, this can be found by taking 20 times the log of the voltage ratio. So,

$$L_{VG} = 20 \log \frac{1}{\sqrt{\left(\dfrac{f_1}{f}\right)^2 + 1}} \tag{4-7}$$

The level at break frequency can be found, just as it was for the LP filter. Then f = f$_1$ and the equation becomes

$$L_{VG} = 20 \log \frac{1}{\sqrt{2}} = -3 \text{ dB}$$

So the level at break frequency, L$_{VG}$ = −3 dB.

The limiting slope of this filter occurs at the lowest frequency (when S approaches zero). Then, in the equation

$$H(S) = \frac{S\mathcal{T}}{(1 + S\mathcal{T})}$$

the S$\mathcal{T}$ term in the denominator becomes negligible compared to the added 1. So the effective LF transfer function becomes

$$H(0) = \frac{S\mathcal{T}}{1} = S\mathcal{T}$$

This means that at each higher octave (double the frequency), the value of the transfer function doubles. This gives a voltage increase per octave of 2 to 1, a gain of 2. The corresponding level gain is given by

$$L_{VG} = 20 \log 2 = 20 \times 0.3 = +6 \text{ dB/octave}$$

Just as in the LP filter, the break frequency is defined as the frequency at which the resistance equals the reactance. Looked at as a concept, this means that the filter has no effect, while the capacitor acts as a shorting link. Only when the frequency has fallen sufficiently for the reactance to be comparable (in fact, equal) to the resistance, does this circuit start to filter out the lower frequencies. This happens when

$$R = X_c$$

or

$$R = \frac{1}{2\pi f_1 C}$$

So,

$$f_1 = \frac{1}{2\pi RC}$$

But,

$$RC = \mathcal{T}$$

Therefore,

$$f_1 = \frac{1}{2\pi \mathcal{T}_1}$$

A typical HP filter response plotted on a frequency base scaled in octaves is shown in Figure 4-7.

Fig. 4-7 Typical
HP filter response

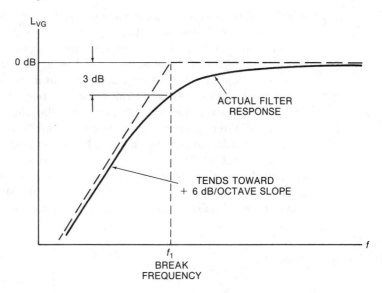

Summary of RC High-Pass Filter Characteristics

1. The break frequency (below which the filtering action becomes apparent) is inversely proportional to the time constant, which equals the product of RC. It is given by

$$f_1 = \frac{1}{2\pi \mathcal{T}_1}$$

   or

$$f_1 = \frac{1}{2\pi RC}$$

2. At break frequency, the level is 3 dB below its maximum value. All frequencies below this are cut off.

3. At low frequencies, the filter's response increases at a rate approaching + 6 dB/ octave as frequency rises.

4. As a general rule, a single element filter has a limiting slope of 6 dB/octave. This is the same as 20 dB/decade (decade means 10 times the frequency).

The Pole/Zero Approach

It is clear that the reactive component (the capacitor in an RC filter or the inductor in an RL filter) is the one that produces the filtering effect. The pole/zero approach derives from the reactive response to frequency change. This response starts from zero frequency and rises if it is an upward slope, or falls if it is a downward slope, at a rate of ± 6 dB/octave. However, because each lower octave is half the frequency of the previous one, and because you can go on halving a value forever before reaching zero, an interesting situation arises.

The HP filtering effect has to be considered as starting at − ∞ dB (called a *zero*, being at the lowest possible level) at zero frequency, and rising by 6 dB at each higher octave. The LP filtering effect has to be thought of as starting at + ∞ dB (called a *pole*, being at the highest level) at zero frequency and dropping by 6 dB at each higher octave. The filtering effects of a single filtering element can, therefore, be visualized from the graphs in Figure 4-8.

Fig. 4-8 Reactive effects of filtering

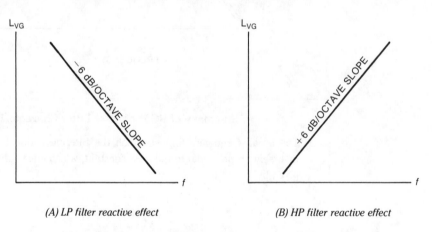

(A) LP filter reactive effect   *(B) HP filter reactive effect*

Now let us consider separately the frequency dependent effect of the resistive and reactive components of these filters. The resistive component is unaffected by frequency; hence, it can be represented graphically by a horizontal line. The reactive component produces either an upward or downward sloping straight line of 6 dB/octave, as previously indicated. These two aspects of a filter can be seen in Figure 4-9, separated into their respective components. The frequency at which

Fig. 4-9 Resistive and reactive aspects of a filter

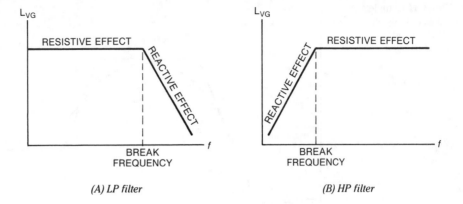

(A) LP filter   *(B) HP filter*

the horizontal and sloping lines intersect, as has already been mentioned, is called the *break frequency*.

Any filter, however complex, can be graphically represented by a number of horizontal and sloping lines. The horizontal lines represent purely resistive effects and the sloping lines purely reactive effects. A graph plotted in this way is called a *Bode plot*, after the name of the man who invented it. The advantage of this construction is that it clearly identifies the break frequencies. It also forms a simplified linear structure into which the actual graph of the filter fits. The relationship between the Bode plot and the actual filter response is shown in Figure 4-10.

Fig. 4-10 Bode plot vs. actual filter response

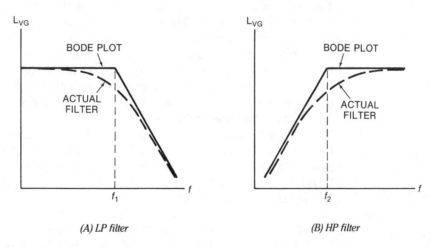

(A) LP filter   *(B) HP filter*

In a more complex filter with many filtering elements, such as a bandpass filter, the relationship between the Bode plot and the actual filter looks like Figure 4-11.

At break frequencies, there tends to be a 3 dB difference between the actual filter response and the Bode plot. Elsewhere, the graphs become progressively closer. Another advantage of the Bode plot is that it clearly isolates the reactive

Fig. 4-11 Complex
filter showing
actual response
and Bode plot

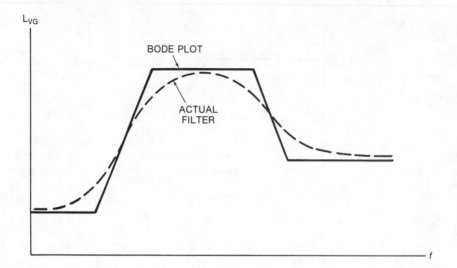

effect of the filter from the resistive effect. Consequently, it is easy to understand all filtering concepts. It is only necessary to visualize each filtering element as a reactive effect causing a slope of 6 dB/octave, starting from zero frequency. However, these do not manifest until their corresponding break frequencies occur. We can see how this takes place by adding to the graph the full reactive effect of each filtering element, starting from zero frequency (see Figure 4-12). The effect of a *pole* is to reduce the slope of the Bode plot by -6 dB/octave where it strikes the graph. The effect of a *zero* is to increase the slope of the Bode plot by $+6$ dB/octave where it strikes the graph.

A steeper cutoff could be produced by having two or more poles or two or more zeros at the same break frequency. Thus, two poles with identical break frequencies would turn down the graph by -12 dB/octave. Similarly, two identical zeros would turn the graph up by $+12$ dB/octave at their break frequency. This effect is illustrated in Figure 4-13.

Any filter, however complex, can also be represented by a combination of four filtering terms and a constant. The constant, often labeled K, is also the DC gain, because it has a purely resistive effect. It is independent of frequency and is, therefore, represented graphically by a horizontal straight line. The reactive filtering terms are as follows:

ST	An upward sloping straight line of $+6$ dB/octave
$1/ST$	A downward sloping straight line of -6 dB/octave
$(ST_c + 1)$	A *zero* producing a change in slope of $+6$ dB/octave
$1/(ST_d + 1)$	A *pole* producing a change in slope of -6 dB/octave

From this list, a numerator term of the form $(ST_c + 1)$ is called a *zero* of the function. At its break frequency (which can be found from its time constant T_c,

Fig. 4-12 Reactive effect of each filtering element

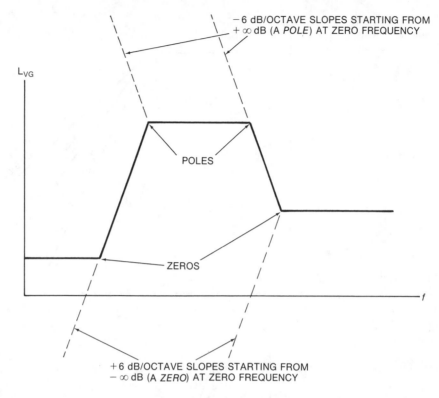

L_{VG}

−6 dB/OCTAVE SLOPES STARTING FROM +∞ dB (A *POLE*) AT ZERO FREQUENCY

POLES

ZEROS

+6 dB/OCTAVE SLOPES STARTING FROM −∞ dB (A *ZERO*) AT ZERO FREQUENCY

f

the coefficient of S), the slope of the Bode increases by +6 dB/octave. A denominator term of the form $1/(S\mathcal{T}_d + 1)$ is called a *pole* of the function. At its break frequency (found from $\mathcal{T}_d$, the coefficient of S), the Bode turns more downward by −6 dB/octave.

It is comparatively easy to write the standard form of a filter from the Bode plot. Let us take a *notch* (stopband) filter for example (Figure 4-14). The break frequencies are f_1, f_2, f_3, and f_4. It can be seen that f_3 and f_4 are poles (denominator terms) because they reduce the slope of the Bode by −6 dB/octave. Also, f_1 and f_2 are zeros (numerator terms) because they increase the slope of the Bode by +6 dB/octave. So the standard form would be

$$H(S) = K\frac{(S\mathcal{T}_1 + 1)(S\mathcal{T}_2 + 1)}{(S\mathcal{T}_3 + 1)(S\mathcal{T}_4 + 1)}$$

Knowledge of filtering is needed not only to design or construct filters, but also because many incidental filtering effects occur within audio systems, and it is necessary to understand filtering in order to be able to deal with them. Also, you may come across technical documents in which the author writes of a coupling capacitor acting as a zero, or a transistor acting as a pole. It is useful to understand what is meant by this. Finally, it has been stated that the break frequencies of a filter and the output level can be calculated simply by finding the

Fig. 4-13 Effect of two or more poles at the same break frequency

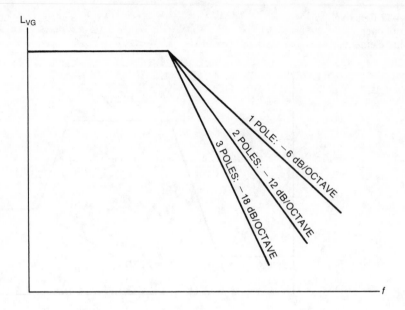

Fig. 4-14 Stopband filter

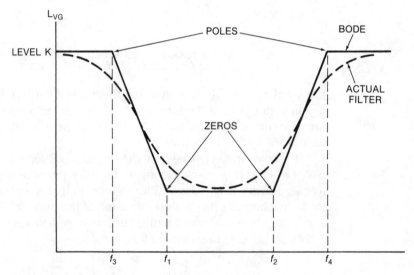

time constants and deriving the transfer function. An example of this procedure is given in the appendix at the end of this book.

Bandpass Filters

A bandpass filter can be made from a high-pass filter followed by a low-pass filter (see Figure 4-15A). Provided the components values are such that the break

Fig. 4-15
Bandpass filter

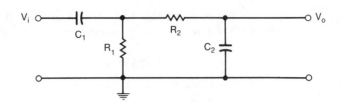

(A) Filter schematic

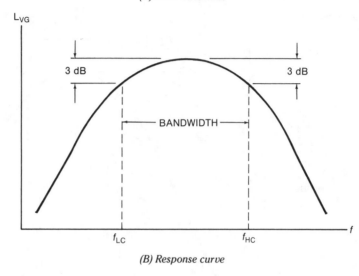

(B) Response curve

frequency of the HP filter is lower than that of the LP filter, the response will be as shown in Figure 4-15B.

The frequencies that are said to be *passed* are those within 3 dB of the maximum value. Hence, the *bandwidth* of a filter includes only the frequencies within this band. The two frequencies at which the curve has fallen by 3 dB are known as *cutoff* frequencies. The low cutoff frequency is f_{LC}, and the high cutoff frequency is f_{HC}. Any frequencies outside this band are said to have been cut off.

In the simple HP or LP filters illustrated earlier in this chapter, the cutoff frequency coincides with the break frequency. In a bandpass filter, especially where the passband is narrow, there is an interference effect between the two break frequencies. As a result, the cutoff frequencies do not coincide with the break frequencies. Because of the interference effect, the levels at the break frequencies can be considerably more than 3 dB below the Bode plot (see Figure 4-16).

In this case, f_1 and f_2 are the break frequencies. The cutoff frequencies are f_{LC} and f_{HC}. The bandwidth occupies the frequency range between these, namely $(f_{HC} - f_{LC})$. It can be seen that the cutoff frequencies do not coincide with the break frequencies here.

It is useful to be able to look at a filtering schematic and tell immediately what type of filter it is. For this purpose, we simply consider three things:

- The high-frequency (HF) response
- The low-frequency (LF) response
- The mid-frequency response

Fig. 4-16
Interference effect in a bandpass filter

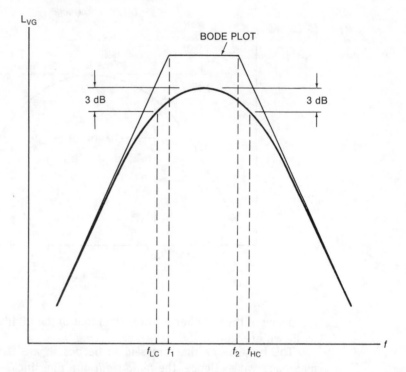

Applying this method to Figure 4-15A:

- HF response: At the highest frequencies, the capacitor reactances fall to zero; therefore, they can be considered shorting links. Then it can be seen that C_2 shorts the output signal to ground and there is no output voltage.
- LF response: At the lowest frequencies, the capacitive reactances become infinitely high, like an open circuit. Consequently, C_1 prevents any signal voltage from passing. So, this filter passes neither the HF nor the LF signals.
- Mid-frequency response: At this frequency, the capacitors have some reactance, so some signal passes through C_1. Also, some output signal develops across C_2.

If the filter passes mid-range signals, but cuts out both high and low frequencies, it must be a bandpass filter. An analysis of a bandpass filter is given in the appendix at the end of this book.

Stopband Filters

These are designed to cut out a certain band of frequencies. An example is the bias trap in a tape recorder's replay circuit. A schematic for this type of filter is shown in Figure 4-17.

Fig. 4-17
Stopband filter
schematic

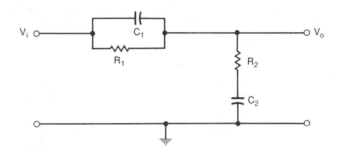

To verify that this acts as a stopband filter, we will apply the method described in the previous section for deriving the filter type from an inspection of the schematic (see Figure 4-17).

- HF response: At the highest frequencies, the capacitors have zero reactance, so they act as shorting links. Consequently, the signal passes directly through C_1. There is no attenuation.
- LF response: At the lowest frequencies, the capacitors have infinite reactance and act as open circuits. The entire signal passes through R_1, and there is no loss of signal across C_2. So again, there is no level loss. This filter passes both the high and low frequencies without loss.
- Mid-frequency response: Here the capacitors have some reactance, so the filter acts as a voltage divider, causing some loss of signal. If a filter reduces the output only at mid frequencies, it must act as we intend, namely as a stopband filter. Sometimes this filter is called a *notch*, because of the appearance of its frequency response curve (see Figure 4-18).

As can be seen from the Bode plot, there are two poles (where the slope is reduced by 6 dB/octave) and two zeros (where the slope increases by 6 dB/octave). The zeros correspond to the break frequencies marked f_1 and f_2 on the graph, the poles to f_3 and f_4. Remembering that zeros are numerator terms and poles are denominator terms, and that the DC gain is unity in this case, it is possible to write the transfer function in standard form from inspection of the Bode plot

Fig. 4-18
Stopband filter
response

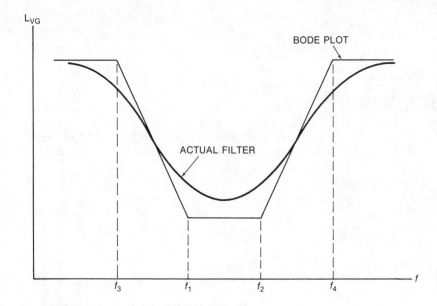

$$\text{Transfer function, } H(S) = \frac{(S\mathcal{T}_1 + 1)(S\mathcal{T}_2 + 1)}{(S\mathcal{T}_3 + 1)(S\mathcal{T}_4 + 1)}$$

For calculation purposes, the output response can be derived from this formula simply by replacing each $(S\mathcal{T}_n + 1)$ term with

$$\sqrt{\left(\frac{f}{f_n}\right)^2 + 1}$$

to obtain its numerical value. f_n is the break frequency that corresponds to a time constant $\mathcal{T}_n$. So,

$$L_{VG} = 20 \log \sqrt{\frac{\left[\left(\frac{f}{f_1}\right)^2 + 1\right]\left[\left(\frac{f}{f_2}\right)^2 + 1\right]}{\left[\left(\frac{f}{f_3}\right)^2 + 1\right]\left[\left(\frac{f}{f_4}\right)^2 + 1\right]}} \quad \text{dB}$$

To find the break frequencies, it is necessary mathematically to find the time constants by obtaining the transfer function V_o/V_i in terms of the component values. Examples of this procedure are included in the appendix.

5 Active Filters

5 Active Filters

Active Filter Characteristics

An active filter is distinguished from a passive filter in that it incorporates an amplifier (usually an op-amp) in its circuit. The result is that it can amplify as well as attenuate a signal. An active high-pass filter can attenuate the low frequencies and amplify the high frequencies. Tone controls and equalizers are usually active for this reason.

In order to make an op-amp into an active filter, it is only necessary to replace either the input resistor or the feedback resistor with a capacitor. This makes the amplifier gain frequency dependent, so it becomes a transfer function. You may remember that the gain of an amplifier is V_o/V_i. When it is frequency dependent, it is called a transfer function.

There are two types of active filters:

- Inverting active filters, in which the input signal is fed into the inverting input
- Non-inverting active filters, in which the input signal is fed into the non-inverting input

We will look at inverting active filters first.

Inverting Active Filters

As was shown in Chapter 3, the gain of an inverting op-amp is given by

$$G_V = \frac{V_o}{V_i} = \frac{R_f}{R_i}$$

When a capacitor is used instead of one of these resistors, we have to write R_f/R_i as Z_f/Z_i. So, for any filter using an inverting op-amp, the inverting active filter transfer function becomes

$$H(S) = \frac{Z_f}{Z_i} \qquad \text{(5-1)}$$

A low-pass active filter is constructed as shown in Figure 5-1A, and its frequency response is shown in Figure 5-1B. In this circuit, $Z_f = 1/SC$ and $Z_i = R$; so the transfer function is

$$H(S) = \frac{Z_f}{Z_i} = \frac{1/SC}{R}$$

Multiplying numerator and denominator by SC,

$$H(S) = \frac{1}{SRC}$$

But $RC = \mathcal{T}$ for these two components; so,

$$H(S) = \frac{1}{S\mathcal{T}} \qquad \text{(5-2)}$$

This forms a downward sloping line, because the transfer function is inversely proportional to the frequency S. The slope is -6 dB/octave because S doubles at each higher octave, and $1/S$ halves (half of the voltage corresponds to -6 dB). For calculation purposes, we can use the fact that

$$S\mathcal{T}_1 = \frac{\omega}{\omega_1} = \frac{f}{f_1}$$

So,

$$H(S) = \frac{1}{S\mathcal{T}_1}$$

can be written

$$H(f) = \frac{f_1}{f}$$

Fig. 5-1 Low-pass (inverting) active filter

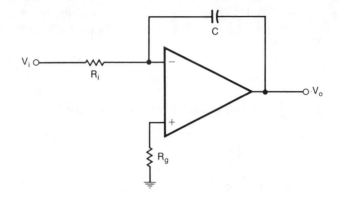

(A) Schematic diagram

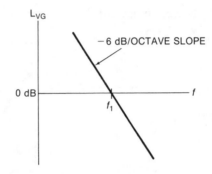

(B) Frequency response

At break frequency (when $f = f_1$),

$$H(f) = \frac{f_1}{f_1} = 1 = 0 \text{ dB}$$

Thus, the downward sloping line cuts the 0 dB level at break frequency. The level at any frequency, f, can be found from

$$L_{VG} = 20 \log \left(\frac{f_1}{f}\right) \text{ dB}$$

where

$$f_1 = \frac{1}{2\pi T_1}$$

and

$$T_1 = RC$$

A high-pass active filter is constructed as shown in Figure 5-2A, and its frequency response is shown in Figure 5-2B. In this filter,

$$H(S) = \frac{Z_f}{Z_i} = \frac{R}{(1/SC)}$$

Multiplying numerator and denominator by SC produces

$$H(S) = \frac{SRC}{1} = SRC$$

But RC = T, so

$$H(S) = S T \qquad\qquad (5\text{-}3)$$

This causes an upward sloping line of +6 dB/octave.

Fig. 5-2
High-pass
(inverting) active
filter

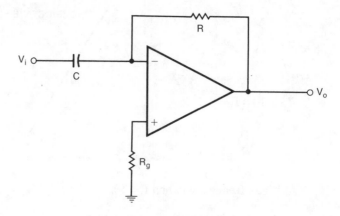

(A) Schematic diagram

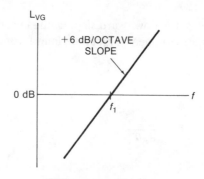

(B) Frequency response

The transfer function of this HP filter is the inverse of the transfer function of the LP filter. Again, at break frequency (when $f = f_1$), the gain becomes 1, which equals 0 dB. So, the rising straight line of $+6$ dB/octave cuts the 0 dB level at break frequency.

Non-inverting Active Filters

If the same set of components were used with the non-inverting input of an op-amp, the resulting frequency response would be different. It was demonstrated in Chapter 3 that the gain of a non-inverting op-amp is given by

$$G_V = 1 + \frac{R_f}{R_i}$$

In a non-inverting active filter,

$$H(S) = 1 + \frac{Z_f}{Z_i}$$

The 1 in this function signifies that, even at the lowest gain, when $Z_f/Z_i = 0$, the transfer function can never be less than 1. Therefore, this type of active filter cannot attenuate; it can only amplify. In some situations, such as obtaining a treble or bass boost, this is just what is required. An LP (non-inverting) active filter is shown in Figure 5-3, together with its frequency response curve.

An HP (non-inverting) active filter is constructed according to the schematic in Figure 5-4A; its frequency response is shown in Figure 5-4B.

One of the applications of non-inverting active filters is in equalizing a magnetic replay head. The combined effect of the narrow head gap and increased wavelength of LF signals causes a replay head to act as a *zero*. In other words, its output falls off by 6 dB/octave as the signal frequency drops. To counteract this, a reproduce equalizer is incorporated, which produces the effect of a *pole*. This boosts the LF by 6 dB/octave as the frequency falls, and so achieves level response (a process called *post emphasis*). However, a *shelving* effect is required, to prevent increasing amplification of infrasonic frequencies, because we don't want to amplify signals that are too low in frequency to be heard. To do so would increase noise and distortion. The shape of the response curve we require is like that shown in Figure 5-5B; the filter schematic is illustrated in Figure 5-5A.

Under DC conditions (when the frequency is zero), the capacitor has an infinitely high reactance and can be considered an open circuit. Under these conditions, it virtually doesn't exist. It is clear that the LF gain (at level K) is produced only by the ratio of the two resistors, R_f/R_i.

When the frequency rises to 15 Hz, the capacitive reactance starts to take effect. At that point, its value has dropped to equality with R_f. The response curve

Fig. 5-3 LP
(non-inverting)
active filter

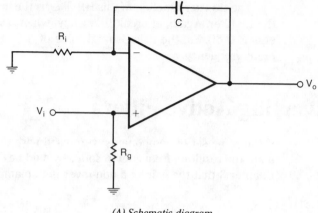

(A) Schematic diagram

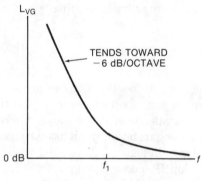

(B) Frequency response curve

starts the downward slope from this frequency. Because a non-inverting op-amp is being used, the gain cannot fall below unity, so the curve flattens out at 15 kHz.

One of the most useful applications of active filters is in the construction of shelving equalizers or tone controls. We will look at these in more detail next.

Shelving Equalizers

A shelving equalizer can either boost or cut the high or low end of the frequency spectrum. In addition, the response curve shelves (flattens out) at the limits of the audio spectrum. This produces the *shelving* effect that gives rise to its name (see Figure 5-6). Normally there are two boost/cut controls, one affecting the HF end of the range, the other affecting the LF end. This type of equalizer is often called a tone control, because it can boost or cut the treble range or the bass range, each independently of the other. Figure 5-6A illustrates the possible shelving effects

Fig. 5-4 HP
(non-inverting)
active filter

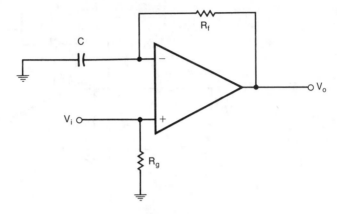

(A) Schematic diagram

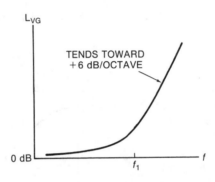

(B) Frequency response curve

available at the high and low ends of the frequency range, while Figures 5-6B and C show the LF and HF filtering circuit schematics.

A single linear potentiometer is used to produce the boost/cut effect by changing the gain of the op-amp. The most effective way to do this is to use the potentiometer as a differential gain control, so that as it increases the feedback resistance, it also reduces the input resistance, or vice versa. Consider the low-frequency stage of the shelving equalizer schematic illustrated in Figure 5-6B.

Ignoring the capacitor for now, notice that as the sliding contact of the potentiometer moves toward point A, the total feedback resistance is reduced, while the input resistance is increased by the same amount. Because the gain of the op-amp is R_f/R_i, this reduces the gain to less than unity, producing LF cut. If the potentiometer slider is moved toward point B, the value of R_f/R_i is increased, increasing the gain and producing LF boost. Because resistance R_1 equals R_2, unity gain is produced when the potentiometer is in the mid position. This gives 0 dB boost or cut.

Fig. 5-5 LP
shelving filter

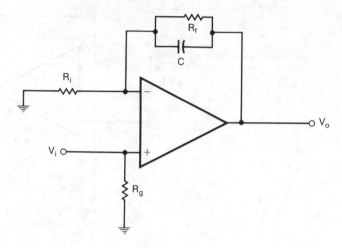

(A) Filter schematic

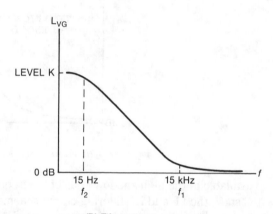

(B) Filter response curve

The next requirement is to limit the effect of this boost/cut facility to low
frequencies only. This is achieved by the capacitor. As the frequency rises, the
reactance of the capacitor falls. The capacitance must, therefore, be chosen so
that, at low frequencies, the reactance is high (as if it were an open circuit), giving
full boost/cut effect to the potentiometer. At mid and high frequencies, the
capacitive reactance falls, so that the potentiometer is effectively short circuited
by the capacitor. Then, the potentiometer has no effect on the gain of the op-amp,
which is held at unity (R_1 being equal to R_2) for all positions of the potentiometer.

The opposite frequency limitations are needed in the high-frequency stage of
the shelving equalizer, illustrated in Figure 5-6C. In place of the capacitor, a
component is required that has the effect of shorting out the potentiometer at low
and mid frequencies, but has a high enough reactance at high frequencies to

Fig. 5-6 Shelving equalizer

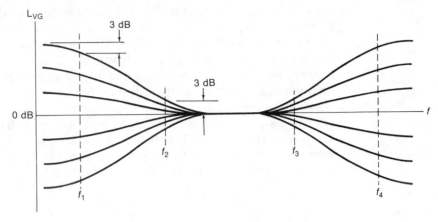

(A) High- and low-frequency response curves

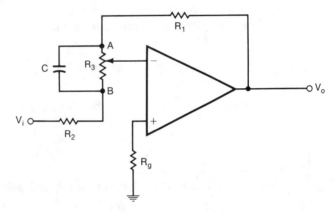

(B) LF filter schematic

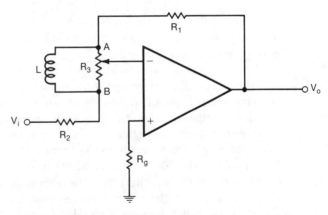

(C) HF filter schematic

allow the potentiometer to take effect. An inductor is the obvious answer, because its frequency response is exactly opposite to that of a capacitor. (Equalizers can be made with more elaborate resistive networks, so that both high- and low-frequency stages can be made entirely with RC circuits. However, we will use an inductor for the HF stage in order to keep the circuitry simple.) The next requirement is to decide on the values of the components, so that the required effect can be produced.

Let us say that we need a maximum boost or cut of 20 dB. This corresponds to a voltage ratio of 10 to 1. In round figures, it is convenient to give R_1 and R_2 values of 1 kΩ each, and R_3 a value of 10 kΩ. The maximum gain (when the potentiometer slider is at position B) is R_f/R_i, which is

$$\frac{(R_1 + R_3)}{R_2}$$

These resistance values produce a ratio of 11,000/1,000, which is approximately 10. The level gain can be calculated from

$$\text{Max boost} = 20 \log \frac{11,000}{1,000} = 20.8 \text{ dB}$$

When the potentiometer contact is in position A, the gain, R_f/R_i, is equal to

$$\frac{R_1}{(R_2 + R_3)}$$

This is 1,000/11,000, the inverse of the previous gain. And the level is now given by

$$\text{Max cut} = 20 \log \frac{1,000}{11,000} = -20.8 \text{ dB}$$

In round figures then, with these resistance values, we achieve the required maximum boost or cut of ±20 dB.

Now it is necessary to decide on the values of the reactive components. Let us take the LF equalizer stage first. At extremely low frequencies, the capacitor acts as an open circuit and maximum equalization control is achieved. Let us establish that the rolloff starts when the frequency has risen to 20 Hz, so that the filtering effect shelves (becomes flattened) at all frequencies below this. It follows that only at or above this frequency is the reactance of the capacitor low enough to be comparable to the 10 kΩ potentiometer. In fact, following the break frequency concepts stated earlier, the capacitive reactance is then equal to the resistance. When this happens, the actual filter response is 3 dB from the maximum value. Therefore, the rolloff frequency is said to occur at 3 dB from shelf value. This is f_1 in Figure 5-6A. Then $X_c = R_3$ and $f = 20$ Hz. The required capacitance can now be found from

$$R = X_c$$

or

$$R = \frac{1}{2\pi fC}$$

So,

$$C = \frac{1}{2\pi fR}$$

Substituting 20 Hz for f, and 10 kΩ for R,

$$C = \frac{1}{2\pi \times 20 \times 10 \times 10^3}$$

$$= 7.96 \times 10^{-7} \text{ farads}$$

$$= 0.796 \ \mu\text{F}$$

In practice, we would use a 0.8 μF value for the capacitor.

We now know all of the component values in the LF equalizer stage. It would be useful, however, to know the higher break frequency. This is the frequency at which maximum boost or cut makes only a ±3 dB level change from the 0 dB level. This is f_2 in Figure 5-6A.

Because we have decided that the maximum boost or cut should be 20 dB, and because a single element filter response rises or falls at 6 dB/octave (which is 20 dB/decade), it follows that f_2 must be one decade (10 times the frequency) above f_1. But f_1 is 20 Hz, so f_2 must be about 200 Hz. This sounds reasonable. It means that only low frequencies below 200 Hz can be affected by the bass control. The control becomes progressively more effective as the frequency falls from 200 to 20 Hz. As far as the HF equalizer stage is concerned, the resistance values are the same. It only remains to find the value of the inductor.

Let us decide that the high shelving frequency should occur at about 15 kHz. This is f_4 in Figure 5-6A. All frequencies above this become flattened out. Then the inductive reactance, which falls as the frequency falls, is equal to the potentiometer resistance at 15 kHz. Below this frequency, the inductor more completely shorts out the potentiometer, so that it has progressively less effect. If $X_L = R_3$ at 15 kHz, we can find the value of the inductor from

$$R = X_L$$

or

$$R = 2\pi fL$$

So,

$$L = \frac{R}{2\pi f}$$

Substituting 15 kHz for f, and 10 kΩ for R,

$$L = \frac{10 \times 10^3}{2\pi \times 15 \times 10^3}$$

$$= 0.106 \text{ henrys}$$

So, we use a 0.1 H inductor in the HF equalizer stage.

Now we need to find out what the lower break frequency is for this HF stage. This is f_3 in Figure 5-6A. At this frequency, the maximum boost or cut does not exceed 3 dB above or below the 0 dB level. At frequencies lower than this, the filter has negligible effect. Again, we can use the fact that the shelf level is ± 20 dB and the filter slope is 20 dB/decade. It follows that the lower break frequency must be one-tenth of the rolloff frequency. One-tenth of 15 kHz is 1.5 kHz. So this HF control acts only above 1.5 kHz and becomes progressively more effective up to 15 kHz. Above that frequency, its effect remains constant.

These two circuits, consisting of the treble and bass controls, are connected in series in the complete equalizer. It doesn't matter in which sequence they are connected; the equalizer will work just as well either way.

These filtering concepts are intended to illustrate how capacitive and inductive reactance can be used in filtering circuits. When these frequency dependent components are inserted into the input or feedback loop of an op-amp, a useful active filter can be made. Just as a top-quality racing driver can improve his or her driving technique by understanding the mechanical principles incorporated in the car, so a top-quality audio engineer can improve his or her ability by understanding the theoretical principles behind filtering techniques.

6 Transformers

6 Transformers

The Voltage Changing Function

To understand how a transformer works, it is necessary to realize that an electric current always surrounds itself with a magnetic field. Current cannot exist without a corresponding magnetic field. The field that develops around a single conductor is comparatively small. When this conductor forms a closely wound coil, however, the field is magnified by the number of turns in the coil. The reason is illustrated by the enlarged cross section through a wire and a coil, shown in Figure 6-1. From this we can see that the fields from the individual turns of a coil combine to produce an amplified field through the core.

Fig. 6-1 Magnetic field surrounding single conductor and coil

(A) Cross section of a single conductor

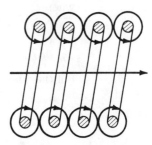

(B) Cross section through four turns of a coil. Each turn adds to the field.

When electric current begins to flow through a coil, some of its energy is converted to magnetic field energy within and around the coil. This extraction of electrical energy causes an induced voltage that opposes the current increase. It is the work done in overcoming this induced opposing voltage that supplies the energy needed to generate the magnetic field.

Conversely, when a magnetic field surrounding a coil degenerates due to a reduction in current flow, some of its energy is transferred back to the coil in the form of electrical energy, inducing a voltage in the direction of the current (opposing its reduction). The magnitude of this induced voltage depends on the rate at which the magnetic field changes and on the number of turns in the coil. It is given by

$$V = N \frac{d\phi}{dt}$$

(6-1)

where
  V   = Induced voltage
  N   = Number of turns in the coil
  $d\phi/dt$ = Rate of change of magnetic field with respect to time

A transformer consists essentially of two coils, a primary and a secondary. The two coils are wound close together so that the changing magnetic field interacts equally with both. A primary coil connected to an AC source produces a fluctuating magnetic field common to both coils. If we call the induced voltage across the primary V_p, and that across the secondary V_s, the ratio of these induced voltages is found from Equation 6-1 by

$$\frac{V_s}{V_p} = \frac{N_s \frac{d\phi}{dt}}{N_p \frac{d\phi}{dt}}$$

where
  N_p = Number of primary turns
  N_s = Number of secondary turns
  $d\phi/dt$ = Rate of change of magnetic field

But the quantity $d\phi/dt$ in this equation cancels; therefore,

$$\frac{V_s}{V_p} = \frac{N_s}{N_p}$$

This demonstrates that the voltage ratio equals the turns ratio in a transformer. This effect can be achieved only under AC conditions. Under DC conditions, the magnetic field remains constant, so $d\phi/dt$ is zero and no voltage can be induced in the secondary.

The voltage changing function is most commonly used in the construction of power supplies. A transistorized circuit requires only about 30 volts. So a line voltage power supply would have, as its first stage, a step-down transformer whose primary at 115 AC volts energizes a secondary coil, to produce just over 30 AC volts. However, a vacuum tube amplifier might requiire 300 volts. In this case, a step-up transformer would be used to convert 115 AC line volts to 300 AC secondary volts.

The Isolation Function

There is no electrical connection between the primary and secondary coils of a transformer. The power transfer takes place by means of magnetic field energy. In the case of a one-to-one transformer, which has a turns ratio of unity, its AC secondary voltage is equal to the AC voltage applied to the primary. It is, therefore, useful not for voltage changing, but for isolation purposes. It can enable a fluctuating DC voltage to flow in the primary while passing only the AC audio component through to the secondary. The DC component, producing no rate of change of magnetic flux, induces no voltage in the secondary.

A typical application consists of transformer coupling a Class A amplifier to its following stage. As described later in Chapter 7, a Class A amplifier requires a direct current through its output transistor at all times. The fluctuations of this current produce the audio signal (see Figure 6-2A). When an audio signal is being carried, the primary circuit current can be thought of as an AC audio signal riding on the shoulders of a DC component. The current is shown graphically in Figure 6-2C.

An isolating transformer can also achieve useful results when installed in the electrical power line that energizes a console. In the resulting balanced line power cable, both conductors are at equal and opposite voltages, instead of one conductor carrying all of the voltage, while the other is effectively grounded. This cuts out noise interference caused by feedback from other equipment and fluorescent lights, and avoids formation of ground loops, which frequently cause hum interference. The method is illustrated in Figure 6-3.

The same method can be used to achieve balanced line transmission between any two audio components, such as a microphone and console input. In these cases, impedance matching can be achieved at the same time. This is because a transformer can not only isolate, it can also match impedance.

To understand how a transformer converts an unbalanced line to a balanced line, consider a transformer with 10 volts induced across the secondary. The only physical requirement is that there must be 10 volts across the secondary terminals. If one end of the secondary is grounded, the other end will be at 10 volts above or below ground potential.

Now consider the transformer illustrated in Figure 6-3. The effect of the grounded center tap is to hold the center of the secondary at 0 volts. Therefore, one terminal of the secondary must be at 5 volts more positive and the other 5 volts more negative. In this way, the requirement of 10 secondary volts is

Fig. 6-2 Coupling
transformer

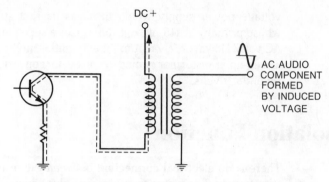

(A) Coupling transformer blocks DC and passes the AC audio signal

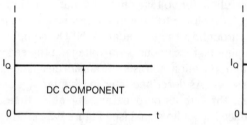

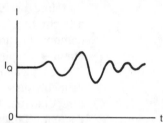

*(B) Primary current, I_Q, under quiescent
conditions, when no audio signal is present*

*(C) Primary current consisting of an AC audio
component riding on a DC quiescent component*

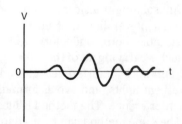

(D) Audio signal voltage induced in the secondary. No DC component is present

Fig. 6-3 Isolating
transformer
supplying power
to a console

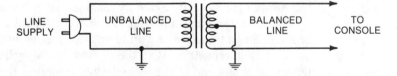

obtained. Of course, the voltages alternate, but they are equally spaced above
and below ground potential. This is what is required for balanced line conduction.
It is achieved simply by holding the center tap of the secondary at ground
potential.

Another use for an isolating transformer is in the breaking of a *ground loop*. Sometimes, after a new audio system is installed, it is discovered that a 60 Hz hum is superimposed on the audio output. Likewise, when a piece of outboard equipment is patched into a system, it might generate unacceptable line hum, which wasn't there before.

These problems are very often created by the formation of a ground loop. A ground loop occurs when there are two paths to ground from any given point in a system. It can be created by two connections to a common metal chassis or by grounding both ends of a shield surrounding a cable. (Only one end should be grounded.) A ground loop looks schematically like the circuit in Figure 6-4.

Fig. 6-4 Creation of a ground loop

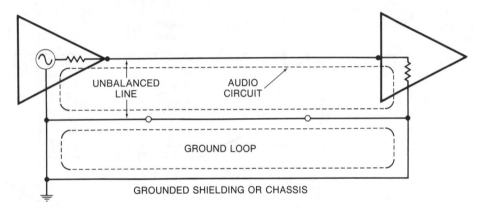

The ground loop acts as a single turn of a coil. In other words, it acts as an inductor. The result is that it creates an induced voltage caused by its interaction with electromagnetic radiation from other equipment. Because most equipment contains a line transformer that leaks electromagnetic radiation, ground loops tend to produce a 60 Hz frequency hum. If you take hold of an audio patch cord or cable and move it slightly, and if this movement alters the intensity of the hum, this is a sure sign of a ground loop.

Often a one-to-one isolating transformer is needed to break such a ground loop and eliminate the line hum. An example of this use of transformer isolation is shown in Figure 6-5. Compare this with Figure 6-4.

The Impedance Matching Function

It is now necessary to say a few words about impedance matching in relation to coupling. Direct coupling involves direct connection between one stage and the next. This is only permissible if the DC voltages and impedances are known to be compatible.

The method more often used is capacitive coupling. This blocks DC voltages, but enables the AC signal to pass. As can be seen from Figure 6-6, the coupling capacitor forms an RC series circuit in conjunction with the input resistance of the following stage, R_i.

Fig. 6-5 Ground loop broken by isolating transformer

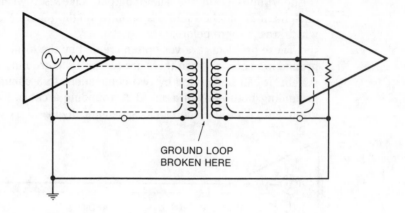

GROUND LOOP
BROKEN HERE

Fig. 6-6 Filtering effect of capacitive coupling

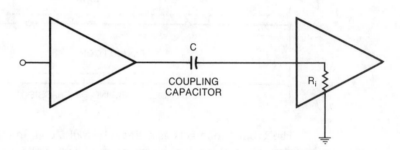

C

COUPLING
CAPACITOR

R_i

The size of the capacitor must be large enough so that its reactance to the lowest audio frequency is only about one-tenth of the impedance value of R_i. In this way, not more than one-tenth of the signal voltage is lost across the coupling capacitor. The size of the capacitor can be calculated from

$$X_c = \tfrac{1}{10}R_i$$

Therefore,

$$\frac{1}{2\pi fC} = \frac{R_i}{10}$$

From this equation, we arrive at

$$C = \frac{10}{2\pi fR_i} \text{ farads (F)}$$

Or,

$$C = \frac{10 \times 10^6}{2\pi \times 15 \times R_i} \, \mu F$$

(at the lowest audible frequency, when f = 15 Hz).

Manufacturers often include a coupling capacitor at the output terminals of their products. The user can then directly connect the output to the input of the next stage, without fear of a DC voltage unbalancing the signal. However, this requires that the output impedance of the previous stage, R_o, be compatible with the input impedance of the following stage, R_L. If these stages are not already impedance matched (see Chapter 1, *The Audio Circuit*), then capacitance coupling will not be acceptable, because any impedance mismatch will remain. However, the use of a suitable transformer can solve many impedance matching problems. Transformer coupling may, therefore, be preferable to capacitance coupling. A transformer blocks DC, allows the AC audio signal to pass, and corrects any impedance mismatch at the same time. The only disadvantage is the cost; still, in some cases, a transformer is well worth its price.

When we think of an inductor, we assume that its impedance is frequency dependent. This is because the reactance of a coil is given by the product of $2\pi fL$. However, if a transformer is correctly impedance matched, its secondary current produces what is called *reflected impedance* in the primary. (Correct impedance matching requires that the primary coil impedance equal the source output impedance, and that the secondary coil impedance equal the load impedance. See Figure 6-7.) Under these impedance matched conditions, the *reflected impedance* produces a primary circuit phase angle, which cancels out the phase angle that would normally be produced by the primary current. Thus, the current in the primary becomes *in phase* at all frequencies. The result is that the primary coil is no longer seen as an inductor by the source. It is seen as a resistor, and its impedance ceases to be frequency dependent. It now acts as a resistive load, whose value is constant at all frequencies. This is how an audio transformer maintains linear response over a wide band of frequencies.

Fig. 6-7 For correct impedance matching, $Z_p = R_o$ and $Z_s = R_L$.

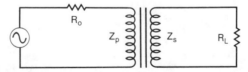

When using a coupling transformer, the primary coil impedance should equal the source output resistance. The secondary coil impedance should equal the load resistance. This method of impedance matching is called *power matching*. The values are not critical; a match within 20 percent is satisfactory.

As described in Chapter 1, maximum power is transferred from a source to a load when $R_L = R_o$ at the interface. Due to reflected impedance, this source sees the primary coil as a resistive load equal to itself. Therefore, it transfers maximum power to the primary. By means of magnetic energy, all of this power is transferred to the secondary. But Z_s acts as the source impedance to the load, and because its value is numerically equal to R_L, it transfers maximum power to the load. The transformer, then, transforms impedances. It enables R_o to see a load equal to itself, while enabling the load to see a source impedance equal to itself.

Under these power matched conditions, there is a definite relationship between the voltage ratio of a transformer and the impedance ratio. At audio frequencies, there is very little energy loss. For calculation purposes, we can assume that an audio transformer is 100 percent efficient. Thus, the power absorbed by the primary equals the secondary power supplied to the load. But $P = V^2/R$ or, at zero phase angle, $R = V^2/Z$. Also, $P = IV$. From these relationships we can make two useful deductions.

$$\text{Primary Power} = \text{Secondary Power}$$

So,

$$\frac{V_p^2}{Z_p} = \frac{V_s^2}{Z_s}$$

or

$$\left(\frac{V_s}{V_p}\right)^2 = \frac{Z_s}{Z_P}$$

Thus,

$$\frac{V_s}{V_p} = \sqrt{\frac{Z_s}{Z_P}}$$

This shows that the voltage ratio, or turns ratio, equals the square root of the impedance ratio. Also, because Primary Power = Secondary Power,

$$I_p V_p = I_s V_s$$

So,

$$\frac{V_s}{V_p} = \frac{I_p}{I_s}$$

(Notice that the current ratio is the inverse of the voltage ratio.) A complete summary of transformer relationships, showing the turns ratio (secondary/primary), is as follows:

$$\text{Turns ratio, } A = \frac{N_s}{N_p} = \frac{V_s}{V_p} = \frac{I_p}{I_s} = \sqrt{\frac{Z_s}{Z_p}}$$

When purchasing audio transformers, the impedance values of the primary and secondary coils are supplied by the manufacturer. Often this data is printed on the side of the metal shielding. You can calculate the corresponding voltage ratio, but it is not necessary to do so. In using an audio transformer for coupling, you need to choose the correct impedances and let the voltage ratio fall where it may.

Many audio transformers used for matching have two or more secondary coils. This gives an opportunity for various possible impedance matches, as shown in Figure 6-8.

Fig. 6-8 Typical matching transformer

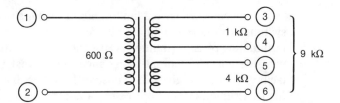

This transformer could match a 600 Ω source circuit (terminals 1 and 2) to the following loads:

1 kΩ   (terminals 3 and 4)
4 kΩ   (terminals 5 and 6)
9 kΩ   (short 4 and 5, and use 3 and 6)

Optionally, the 600 Ω could be used as the secondary, and any of the other coils as the primary.

You might be surprised to learn that both secondary coils in series produce a total impedance of 9 kΩ, and not 5 kΩ. Because the turns are added and the voltages are directly proportional to the turns, the two secondary voltages are added. However, the voltages are proportional to the square root of the impedances, so the roots of the two impedances must be added. Their sums must then be squared to convert the resultant voltage back to impedance. The total secondary impedance is given by

$$(\sqrt{Z_1} + \sqrt{Z_2})^2$$

or

$$(\sqrt{1,000} + \sqrt{4,000})^2$$

Another option is available for matching a source to a primary. If the primary coil impedance is too great to be correctly matched, a *building-out* resistor can be added in series with the source. This resistor should be of sufficient value to raise the resistance of the source to that of the primary coil; then, good match and linear frequency response will be achieved. For example, if the source $R_o = 600$ Ω and the transformer Z_p = 1 kΩ, then a 400 Ω building-out resistor, R_p, is needed. ($R_o + R_p$ = Z_p, or $600 + 400$ = 1 kΩ. See Figure 6-9.)

Fig. 6-9 A building-out resistor used for primary impedance matching

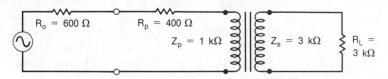

Some consoles have a built-in 600 Ω load resistor, which can be inserted by a switch as either a building-out resistor (in series with the source) or as a terminating resistor (shunted across the output terminals, effectively paralleling it with the console's output impedance). For transformer coupling this is a useful facility, because it gives the console three possible effective output impedances. Let us assume that the console has a natural output impedance of 600 Ω. By using the building-out resistor, this can be increased to 1,200 Ω. By using the terminating resistor, this can be reduced to 300 Ω.

If in doubt, it is a good idea to run a quick frequency response test. Put a constant level signal through the system at, say, 20 Hz, 1 kHz, and 20 kHz. If there is loss of low or high frequencies, try using the additional resistor, first in building-out position, then in terminating position, and see which gives the most level response.

Bandpass Characteristics

Transformers designed for audio frequency work are constructed around an iron core. This concentrates the magnetic field, resulting in increased effectiveness and reduced production cost. At radio frequencies, an iron core is not necessary, and many RF transformers are made with air cores. This is acceptable because the rate of change of magnetic flux is greater at higher frequencies.

Although the efficiency of an iron cored transformer is nearly 100 percent, there are two significant sources of energy loss. One consists of hysteresis loss in the iron core. The other consists of coupling loss. (See the appendix for a detailed description of hysteresis.)

Hysteresis loss results from internal friction in the iron as the magnetic flux reverses. This draws additional magnetizing current from the source. Because the required magnetic field intensity increases at low frequencies (to maintain the rate of change of flux), this current loss becomes significant at low frequencies.

Coupling loss, on the other hand, occurs significantly at high frequencies. This is because the fluctuating magnetic field extends farther at high frequencies; consequently, some of the magnetic field energy fails to couple with the secondary. This unused energy is dissipated as electromagnetic radiation.

The result of these losses causes an audio transformer to act as a bandpass filter. The output remains flat over the audio frequency range, but falls off at very low and very high frequencies.

We will ignore the DC resistance of the coils, because they are small compared to the source and load resistances, and also because they are not frequency dependent. Taking hysteresis and coupling losses into account, the equivalent circuit of a step-down transformer would look like that in Figure 6-10, where:

R_o = Output resistance of generator (source)
R_L = Load resistance
L_M = Equivalent inductance, drawing extra magnetizing current due to hysteresis loss
L_S = Equivalent inductance, representing coupling loss leakage

Fig. 6-10
Transformer
equivalent circuit

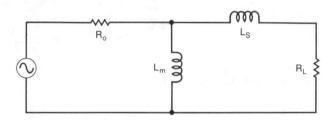

L_M is shunted across the generator terminals because its effect is to draw additional current from the source. L_S is in series with the load because it reduces the voltage across the load. The low- and high-frequency equivalent circuits are illustrated in Figure 6-11.

Fig. 6-11
Low- and
high-frequency
equivalent circuits

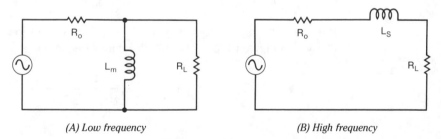

(A) Low frequency   *(B) High frequency*

At low frequencies, the reactance of L_S becomes negligible, so it can be ignored. But when the reactance of L_M becomes small, it draws far more current from the source. Consequently, there is a greater voltage drop across R_o, and this effect reduces the voltage across R_L.

At high frequencies, the reactance of L_M is so high that it acts as an open circuit; therefore, it can be ignored. But the high reactance of L_S reduces the voltage across R_L, so this effect is now significant. The low-frequency equivalent circuit consequently acts as a high-pass filter, cutting off the low frequencies. The high-frequency equivalent circuit acts as a low-pass filter, cutting off the high frequencies. The effect of both is to produce a wide-band bandpass filter.

The characteristic structure built into these transformers by the manufacturer is designed to ensure that the full range of audio frequencies is included within the bandwidth. This only happens, however, when both transformer coils are correctly impedance matched. If either coil is severely mismatched, the passband moves either up or down the audio spectrum, causing loss of low or high frequencies. To illustrate this, we will derive an expression for the cutoff frequencies of the equivalent circuits in Figure 6-11.

At low frequencies, the break frequency of the circuit in Figure 6-11A can be found using the filter analysis method given in Chapter 4. The derivation of the transfer function that results is given in the appendix at the end of the book. By this method, the transfer function appears as

$$H(S) = \frac{R_L}{R_o + R_L} \left(\frac{SL_M \left[\dfrac{R_o + R_L}{R_o R_L} \right]}{SL_M \left[\dfrac{R_o + R_L}{R_o R_L} \right] + 1} \right) \tag{6-2}$$

This is a standard HP filter of the form

$$H(S) = K \frac{S\mathcal{T}}{S\mathcal{T} + 1}$$

It is clear that the coefficient of S is $\mathcal{T}$. So, by comparison of forms,

$$\mathcal{T} = L_M \left[\frac{R_o + R_L}{R_o R_L} \right]$$

However, the break frequency (and in this case, the low cutoff frequency) is always found from $1/2\pi\mathcal{T}$. So, the low cutoff frequency is

$$f_{LC} = \frac{1}{\dfrac{2\pi L_M (R_o + R_L)}{R_o R_L}}$$

Thus,

$$f_{LC} = \frac{R_o R_L}{2\pi L_M (R_o + R_L)} \tag{6-3}$$

It is comparatively easy to find the break frequency of the equivalent HF circuit shown in Figure 6-11B, because this is a simple RL series circuit. In this case, the time constant is simply L/R. So,

$$T = \frac{L_s}{R_o + R_L}$$

Thus,

$$f_{HC} = \frac{1}{\dfrac{2\pi L_S}{R_o + R_L}}$$

Therefore,

$$f_{HC} = \frac{R_o + R_L}{2\pi L_S} \qquad \text{(6-4)}$$

These transfer functions and the resulting time constants will shortly be used to examine the effect on bandwidth of a transformer impedance mismatch. Due to the physical problems inherent in transformer construction, a large ratio transformer is highly sensitive to impedance mismatching. A low ratio transformer has a much larger bandwidth; therefore, impedance matching is not critical.

One situation in which a matching transformer must be precisely matched is at the output from a vacuum tube power amplifier. Here, the tubes, with an output impedance of about 6 kΩ, are feeding a speaker of about 8 Ω. A high ratio transformer is, therefore, needed. The construction of such a transformer, with the necessary bandwidth, is so difficult that the manufacturers have to use a multitapped secondary. The schematic of such a transformer is shown in Figure 6-12.

Fig. 6-12
Loudspeaker
matching
transformer

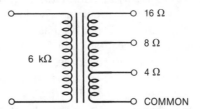

When connecting a loudspeaker to the secondary, the common terminal is always used. The other output terminal is chosen to match the speaker impedance. Therefore, a 4 Ω speaker is connected between the 4 Ω output and common. Of course, two 8 Ω speakers could be connected in parallel between the 4 Ω output and common, or in series between the 16 Ω output and common. Series connection requires a positive (+) terminal from one speaker to be connected to a negative (−) terminal on the other. In parallel, the two + terminals are connected, and the two − terminals are connected (see Figure 6-13). If the speaker polarities are wrongly connected, phase cancellation results in loss of low frequencies.

Fig. 6-13 Phase matching two loudspeakers

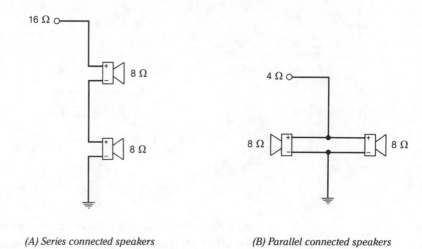

(A) Series connected speakers   *(B) Parallel connected speakers*

Because impedance matching is so critical with high ratio transformers, you have to watch out for this type of situation. If, for instance, you need to record from the loudspeaker terminals of a tube amplifier, it is important not to connect the 16 Ω output terminals directly to a 600 Ω (or more) recorder input, without using a 16 Ω load. Calculating the cutoff frequency from Equations 6-3 and 6-4, and using L_M = 0.085 H and L_S = 0.060 H, the indication is that all low frequencies below 1 kHz will be cut off. For correct results, it is necessary to connect a dummy 16 Ω (10 W) load resistor across the amplifier output, in parallel with the output cable. Then, the full frequency response will be restored.

However, if an output transformer is built onto a transistorized amplifier, there will be no problem. The low turns ratio needed to match a 1 Ω power transistor to a 4 Ω speaker has such a wide bandwidth that practically any load above 4 Ω is acceptable. In fact, manufacturers often specify the load as being "4 Ω or more." In this case, you can connect the power amplifier directly to a recorder input, without a speaker load, and still obtain full frequency bandwidth.

Another situation in which a high ratio matching transformer is needed occurs when using a high impedance microphone or guitar pickup with a long mic cable. A microphone matching transformer is needed then to change the high output impedance of the mic to the low impedance that must be fed to a long cable. (The necessity for this will be discussed later.) At the other end of the cable, another transformer is needed to match the low impedance source to the high impedance pre-amplifier input. Without this input transformer, incorrect loading of the microphone transformer could restrict the available bandwidth. A schematic of the system illustrates the arrangement in Figure 6-14. (The letter *Z* refers to impedance.)

On the other hand, a low impedance microphone can be directly connected to a long microphone cable. A step-up transformer might be used at the

Fig. 6-14
Transformer
matching a
high-impedance
mic to a long
transmission cable

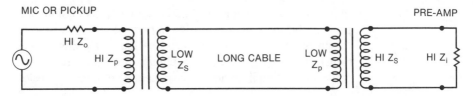

pre-amplifier input (this would slightly reduce the noise level), or it need not be used. In this case, transformer matching is optional.

Now I should explain why a long transmission cable must be fed by a low impedance source. When two conductors in a cable run close together, there is a small amount of capacitance between them. The capacitance increases in proportion to the length of the cable, so a long cable produces significant capacitance between the two conductors. When this cable is fed from a microphone (or any audio generator), the equivalent circuit looks like that in Figure 6-15.

Fig. 6-15 Filtering
effect of
transmission line,
where R_o is
source output
impedance and C
is cable
capacitance

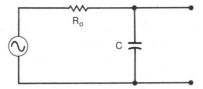

By looking back at Chapter 4, we can see that this is, in fact, the circuit of an LP filter. It is not that we want to include an LP filter; we can't help it. So we must ensure that the resulting cutoff frequency is above the highest audible frequency of about 15 kHz. In any capacitor, the reactance drops as the frequency rises; the cutoff point is reached when the reactance is low enough to equal the resistance of R_o. The level at this frequency is 3 dB down. All higher frequencies are cut off.

In practice, we do not wish to lose even 3 dB from the response of our microphone at 15 kHz. One-tenth of the signal voltage is the maximum acceptable HF loss. If fed by a low-impedance microphone of 100 Ω, the total cable reactance at 15 kHz should, therefore, be ten times this value (namely, 1 kΩ). Using typical microphone cable, it works out that the maximum acceptable cable length would be 200 feet. (The cable capacitance would then be so high that the reactance across the cable would be reduced to 1 kΩ.)

However, if the output impedance of the microphone were 1 kΩ (ten times higher), then the frequency at which one-tenth of the signal is lost would be ten times lower (namely, 1.5 kHz). This is obviously unacceptable because all higher audio frequencies would experience excessive loss. (Remember that frequency is inversely proportional to capacitive reactance. Therefore, ten times the reactance would occur at one-tenth of the frequency.) This is why it is necessary to use a low impedance source for long audio cable transmission. Matching transformers provide the solution, where high impedance sources have to be used.

In many situations, where no serious matching problems exist, the use of transformer or capacitance coupling is optional. The need to control cost favors capacitance coupling; however, some advantages of transformers are

1. The bandpass characteristic limits frequencies to within fixed parameters.
2. Isolation from other circuits is complete. This helps to prevent ground loops.
3. Although capacitors block most of the DC, electrolytic capacitors often leak a certain amount of DC voltage. Transformers block DC voltages completely.

Avoiding Transformer Generated Distortion

One aspect of transformers hasn't been mentioned yet. That is the need to avoid overload distortion. A piece of iron can be magnetized only up to a certain level. It is then fully magnetized and no additional magnetizing force will increase its magnetization. It is said to be magnetically saturated, meaning it contains the greatest amount of magnetic energy it can hold. If more magnetic energy has to be stored, more iron is needed. That is why high-power transformers have large iron cores, and are heavy and expensive.

If a transformer is asked to transmit more than its rated power, the iron in the core can become magnetically saturated. The result is that during periods when the primary current approaches its peaks, more and more of the core saturates and fails to transmit the corresponding energy increase to the secondary. This gives rise to a peculiar distorted waveform. The effect is illustrated in Figure 6-16.

Fig. 6-16
Distorted
waveform
resulting from
power overload

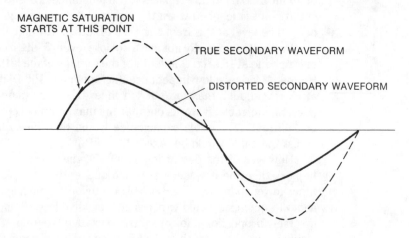

MAGNETIC SATURATION
STARTS AT THIS POINT

TRUE SECONDARY WAVEFORM

DISTORTED SECONDARY WAVEFORM

An unusual characteristic of this type of distortion is that it occurs first at low frequencies. This is because, at low frequencies, a phase angle develops and magnetic peaks become higher in order to transmit the same amount of power. So, if in doubt as to the power handling ability of a transformer, test at 15 Hz with the maximum signal voltage you are likely to use. If the output wave, seen on an oscilloscope, looks good, you can be sure that all higher frequencies will behave correctly. Remember to test for overload distortion at 15 Hz, not at the normal test frequency of 1 kHz.

Summary of Transformer Applications

1. Transformers are used in power supplies to transform AC voltages either up or down. Because only AC voltages can be transformed, both the primary input and secondary output are in AC form.
2. A one-to-one transformer can be used to isolate one stage or component from another. This can eliminate noise interference by preventing ground loop formation.
3. Transformers can convert unbalanced lines to balanced line transmission. This reduces electrical interference and also helps to eliminate noise.
4. Transformers are often used to couple one stage to the next. The transformer completely blocks DC voltage, while allowing the AC audio signal to pass. A coupling transformer can also correct an impedance mismatch; however, high turns ratio transformers need to be impedance matched to their source and load, to avoid loss of high or low frequencies.
5. The power handling ability of any transformer depends on the amount of iron in its core. Test for possible overload distortion at the lowest audio frequency of 15 Hz, not the usual test frequency of 1 kHz.

7 Semiconductors

7 Semiconductors

Diodes

Atoms consist of a positively charged nucleus surrounded by orbiting negatively charged electrons. The number of electrons equals the number of protons in the nucleus, so the positive and negative charges balance. Electric current consists of a flow of *free* electrons. *Free* means released from orbital constraint around a nucleus.

Atoms prefer to have eight electrons in the outer *valent* orbit. Beyond that number, they start an additional outer ring. If this contains one electron, they have one more than the eight preferred, so they easily lose the extra electron through thermal agitation (heat vibration). Therefore, this type of material contains many free electrons, which act as current carriers. Such materials make good conductors.

Atoms that have seven electrons in their outer orbit are reluctant to lose one (their preference being to gain one, making eight). This type of material contains practically no free electrons; thus, it has good insulation properties.

Atoms that contain four electrons in their outer valent orbit are indifferent to losing or gaining one electron. If they lose one, they have three. This is three above what exists in the complete inner ring of eight. If they gain one, they have five. This is three below the preferred number of eight. These atoms, with four valent electrons, are called *semiconductors*.

A PN junction diode consists of two wafers of a semiconductor element fused together. The two halves of the diode are each impregnated with a different element. This process is called *doping*. A small quantity of doping material is evenly diffused throughout the semiconductor material.

There are two types of doping material. One contains five valent electrons (called pentavalent doping). The other contains three valent electrons (called trivalent doping). Where a pentavalent atom replaces a semiconductor atom, there are five valent electrons instead of four. Consequently, one free negative current carrier is produced by each doping atom. This type of doped semiconductor material is called *N-type* material, because it carries a large number of extra electrons, which are negative current carriers. On the other hand, where a trivalent atom replaces a semiconductor atom, there are only three valent electrons instead of four. This leaves a *hole*, which attracts electrons and acts as a positive current carrier. This type of doped semiconductor material is called *P-type* material, because it contains a large number of positive current carriers.

Briefly then, a diode consists of a wafer of N-type semiconductor material fused at a junction to a wafer of P-type semiconductor material. This produces a junction that offers extremely high resistance to current flow in one direction, and extremely low resistance in the other. In effect, it acts as a one-way street, allowing current to flow only in one direction. When a voltage is applied to the diode in a polarity that permits current to flow, it is called *forward biased*; a polarity in which no current can flow is called *reverse biased*. The schematic symbol for a diode is shown in Figure 7-1. The arrowhead indicates the direction in which conventional current can flow, which is from positive (+) to negative (−). The results of forward biasing are illustrated in Figure 7-2. (Note that like charges repel and unlike charges attract.)

Fig. 7-1
Schematic symbol
for a diode

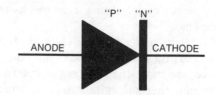

Fig. 7-2 Effect of
biasing a PN
junction

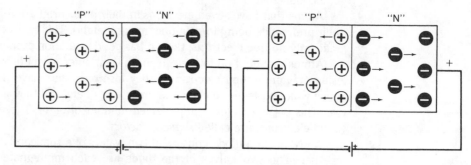

(A) Forward biased. Current carriers forced toward the junction experience little resistance in crossing over, so current flows.

(B) Reverse biased. Current carriers being pulled away from the junction cannot cross over, so no current flows.

These current carriers produced in the semiconductor material by doping are called *majority carriers*. There are also a few free electrons and holes, inherent in the pure semiconductor material itself, that have been released by thermal agitation. These are called *minority carriers*. Therefore, to say that no current flows in reverse bias polarity is not 100 percent accurate. In fact, a very small amount of current flows when reverse biased, due to the minority carriers only. While under forward biased conditions, current flows as a result of both majority and minority carriers.

One other property of PN junction diodes needs to be mentioned. This is the spontaneous creation of ions (charged atoms) in close proximity to the junction, even when no external voltage is applied. Due to the attraction between opposite charges, some electrons cross over and occupy some of the holes on the other side of the junction. The effect is two-fold.

1. It produces a small area on each side of the junction where the majority carriers are missing, or cancelled out. This is called the *depletion zone*, because here the number of carriers has been depleted.

2. It also causes a voltage to develop spontaneously across the junction.

To see why this voltage occurs, consider the doping material. Pentavalent doping atoms have five electrons and five corresponding protons. Consequently, their net charge is zero. Similarly, trivalent doping, with three valent electrons, has only three corresponding protons, also with no resultant charge. However, as soon as some electrons on the N side cross over the junction, negative charge is lost and a positive charge results. When these electrons fill holes on the P side, the positive charges become cancelled and a negative charge results. This causes a *barrier potential* to occur (see Figure 7-3).

Fig. 7-3 Enlarged view of a PN junction

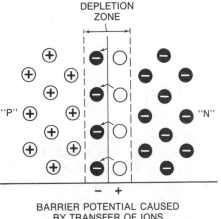

DEPLETION
ZONE

"P"   "N"

− +

BARRIER POTENTIAL CAUSED
BY TRANSFER OF IONS
ACROSS JUNCTION

The barrier effect of this spontaneously generated voltage is experienced when the diode starts to be forward biased. In Figure 7-3, forward bias occurs when a + polarity is applied to the P side and a − polarity to the N side. However, there is already a reverse bias that has been spontaneously produced at the junction. This acts as a barrier to current flow, even when forward biased. The result is that the applied forward bias voltage must be higher than the barrier potential before any current can flow. If it is lower (or reversed), the diode is said to be *cut off*. This barrier potential is of the same magnitude as the cutoff voltage, which depends on the semiconductor material. Silicon diodes have a cutoff voltage of about 0.6 V and germanium diodes have a cutoff voltage of about 0.2 V.

The current/voltage graph of a diode is shown in Figure 7-4. As can be seen from the graph, current increases linearly in proportion to bias voltage once the

Fig. 7-4 Diode characteristic curve

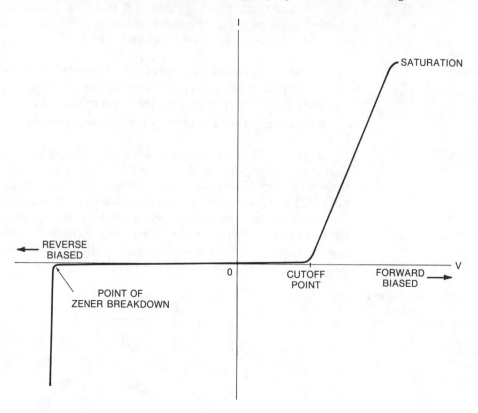

cutoff point has been passed in the forward bias direction. Below cutoff voltage and covering a considerable extent of reverse bias, there is practically no current flow at all. However, if too much reverse bias is applied, there is a sudden increase in reverse current at the point of *zener breakdown*. This happens when the applied reverse polarity voltage reaches a level at which the semiconductor insulation breaks down. The diode is then said to be *zenering*. This property enables a *zener diode* to output a constant voltage within a circuit under certain conditions. This characteristic is used in voltage regulated power supplies.

Transistors

A transistor consists basically of two diodes back to back, which form a sandwich of P- and N-type material. This can be made in two ways (see Figure 7-5).

Fig. 7-5 Types of transistors

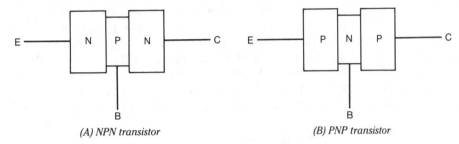

(A) NPN transistor   *(B) PNP transistor*

Current flow is from the *emitter* through the *base* and out through the *collector*. These terminals are labeled E, B, and C, respectively. The two types of transistors are distinguishable by the direction of the arrow in the schematic symbols (see Figure 7-6). This indicates the direction of conventional current flow (holes flow). Of course, electron flow is in the opposite direction. It is useful to remember that electrons always flow in the opposite direction from the arrows, in the symbols both for diodes and transistors.

Fig. 7-6
Schematic symbol
for a transistor

(A) NPN transistor   *(B) PNP transistor*

In the case of an NPN transistor, forward bias for the E/B junction requires that the P material of the base be more positive than the N material of the emitter. Electrons can then flow through this junction in the opposite direction from the arrow. Because electron flow has to be in this direction, certain DC voltages must be present. The required polarities and current paths are shown in Figure 7-7. The double polarity sign at the collector is intended to show that the collector voltage must be greater than the same polarity at the base. Also indicated is a small (approximately 2 percent) current leakage from the base.

Fig. 7-7 Electron
flow and
polarities in
transistors

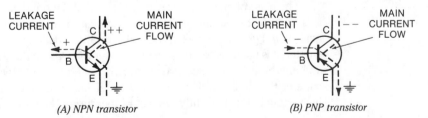

(A) NPN transistor   *(B) PNP transistor*

It is the junction between the emitter and base that is the key to controlling the current flow through a transistor. The bias voltage across this junction is called the *bias* of the transistor. When this bias, V_{EB}, is below cutoff, no current flows and the transistor is cut off. As can be seen from the graph of diode current in Figure 7-4, once bias voltage has risen to cutoff point, any increase produces a corresponding increase in current. It is the same with the transistor. Above cutoff point, the current flow is linearly proportional to bias voltage.

When I speak of current flow in this analysis, I am referring to electron flow (as opposed to *holes* flow, which is in the opposite direction). Consider an NPN transistor in which the bias voltage (V_{EB}) is below cutoff. No current can flow from E to B; however, there is a quiescent voltage between B and C that could cause current to flow between these two points. This doesn't happen because the polarities are such that the B/C junction is reverse biased. Thus, no current can flow through either junction while V_{EB} is below cutoff.

Now consider an NPN transistor in which the bias voltage is above cutoff. Electrons immediately flow from the emitter into the base (through the now forward biased E/B junction). Because the base is extremely thin and only lightly doped, a minute fraction of this initial charge of electrons is enough to neutralize the majority carriers (holes) in the base. This cancels the effect of the PN junction between the base and collector. The result is that the rest of the incoming current is conducted out through the collector by its higher positive polarity. So, in effect, the base/collector junction ceases to be a diode junction after electrons from the emitter flow into the base. This junction returns to reverse bias only when no more current flows, which happens when V_{EB} falls below cutoff.

So, the collector current, I_c, is determined by the current that flows through the E/B junction, I_E. The base, being wafer thin, offers high resistance to current flow through its edge connection. Only about 2 percent leaks out this way. The remaining 98 percent goes out through the collector.

A transistor can conduct current only if the correct quiescent voltages are present at its terminals. As an analogy, it would be useless to press the accelerator of a car whose engine is switched off. It wouldn't matter how hard the accelerator were pressed; the car wouldn't move. Similarly, with a transistor, if the correct quiescent voltages are not present, the transistor won't amplify a signal. (Therefore, one of the first things to do when troubleshooting is to check that the quiescent voltages are correct.)

In an NPN transistor, the collector voltage should be from 5 to 30 V more positive than the emitter. In a PNP, it should be more negative by the same amount. If the collector voltage is 0, there is a break in the power supply to the collector.

The bias voltage, V_{EB}, is far more critical and more difficult to measure. Whereas it is possible to use an ordinary multimeter to measure the voltage between the emitter and ground, between the collector and ground, or between the collector and emitter, it is not possible to use a multimeter to measure the voltage between the base and anything. This is because there is high resistance between the base and other parts of the circuit. Although a multimeter has moderately high resistance, it is not high enough. Consequently, the act of measuring the base voltage changes it, and a completely false reading is obtained. Either a VTVM (vacuum tube voltmeter) with a DC voltage range or a FET meter must be used. (It would be useful for anyone wanting to do serious audio work to own a FET meter.)

Both the VTVM and FET meters use a built-in amplifier to power the meter movement, so they draw practically no current and have almost infinitely high input resistance. The advantage of a FET meter is that it is as portable as a multimeter and cheaper than a VTVM. It contains its own *field effect transistor* (FET) amplifier, which is powered by an internal battery.

If either a VTVM or FET meter is available, the bias voltage between base and emitter can be measured. In an amplifier, the quiescent bias voltage should be at or just above cutoff point. In an NPN transistor, the base should be 0.6 V (for silicon) or 0.2 V (for germanium) more positive than the emitter. In a PNP transistor, the base should be more negative than the emitter by this amount. From consideration of these quiescent voltages, it is possible to tell if a semiconductor is conducting. For example, in Figure 7-8, can you tell if these semiconductors are conducting? The answers are in the box below. (The elemental abbreviations of Si for silicon and Ge for germanium are used.)

Fig. 7-8 Can you tell if these semiconductors are conducting?

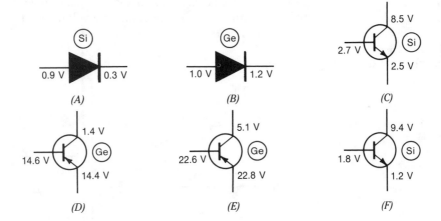

Answers to Figure 7-8

(A)   Yes. Bias is 0.6 V forward.

(B)   No. Bias is 0.2 V, which is numerically above cutoff, but in the reverse bias polarity. (Electrons can flow only in the opposite direction from the arrow.)

(C)   No. Bias is 0.2 V. Although it is in the forward polarity, it is below cutoff. 0.6 V is required for silicon.

(D)   No. Bias is 0.2 V in the reverse polarity.

(E)   Yes. Bias is 0.2 V in the forward polarity.

(F)   Yes. Bias is 0.6 V in the forward polarity.

Common Emitter Amplifiers

There are three basic configurations in which a transistor amplifier can be made. Each has its own characteristics, and these determine the type of application for which it is suitable.

The configuration most often used for general purpose amplification is the *common emitter*. This circuit diagram (using an NPN transistor) is shown in Figure 7-9, where:

R_1 is the load resistor, across which the output voltage develops.

R_2 is the emitter, or stabilizing resistor. It is needed to prevent self-destruction of the transistor by thermal runaway.

R_3 and R_4 form a voltage divider, producing a voltage at the base that ensures correct forward bias.

C_1 and C_2 are coupling capacitors. These pass the audio signal while blocking any DC voltage.

C_3 is a by-pass capacitor. It by-passes any audio signal that might develop across R_2 to ground, thus cutting out any voltage fluctuations at the emitter.

Fig. 7-9 Common emitter amplifier

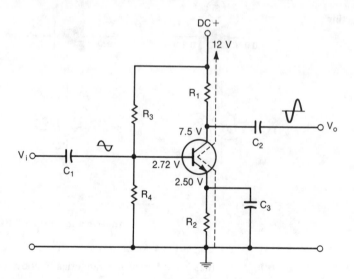

In order to understand how this circuit amplifies, look first at the quiescent DC voltages at the three terminals of the transistor. The bias voltage between the base and emitter is 0.22 V, so this must be a germanium transistor. The transistor conducts about half its maximum current under quiescent conditions. The negative (electron) current flow is shown as a dotted line.

The audio signal enters through C_1. If we assume that the amplitude of this wave is about .02 V, then the first half-cycle, being positive, will raise the voltage at the base by .02 V, from 2.72 V to 2.74 V. This increases the forward bias from .22 V to .24 V, which in turn increases the current flow through the transistor.

This increased current, which flows through the load resistor R_1, produces an increased voltage drop across R_1. Notice that under quiescent conditions, the voltage drop across R_1 is 4.5 V; however, when this increased current flows, it produces a greater voltage drop.

Because the 12 volts at the top of R_1 is a battery or regulated power supply voltage, it cannot change, so the 7.5 V voltage at the bottom of R_1 drops. In fact, it drops to about 3.5 V (a 4 V drop) at the peak of the first half-cycle.

In the second half-cycle, the signal voltage applied through C_1 is negative, so the base voltage now drops by .02 V, to 2.70 V. This reduces the forward bias from 0.22 V to 0.20 V, and this, in turn, reduces the current flow. The consequently reduced current reduces the voltage across R_1 by the same amount as the increase of the first half-cycle. So the voltage at the bottom of R_1 goes up toward the 12 V supply by 4 V, to 11.5 V.

Now the output waveform at the collector is 180° out of phase with the input signal. There is also considerable voltage amplification. An input peak-to-peak signal amplitude of .04 V produces an output peak-to-peak signal amplitude of 8 V. So the voltage gain is in the ratio of 8 to .04, which is 200.

Although R_2 has been described as the emitter resistor, or stabilizing resistor, its function hasn't been fully described. The need for its presence derives from the fact that semiconductor material becomes less resistant to current as its temperature rises. When current flows through a transistor, its temperature inevitably rises. Because of the consequent reduction in its internal resistance, more current flows. This, in turn, leads to a higher temperature, a further reduction in resistance, and a further increase in current. This process creates an unstable cycle that leads to eventual burnout of the transistor due to *thermal runaway*. The emitter resistor is able to prevent this.

When the current flow through the transistor increases, there is, of course, an equal increase in current through the emitter resistor, R_2. This causes an increase in voltage across it, which pushes the voltage at the emitter toward that of the base, thus reducing the forward bias. This forms a *fail-safe* system that automatically reduces the forward bias to cutoff, if the current should reach a high enough level. This prevents thermal runaway, because it ensures that the current through the transistor cannot exceed a fixed amount.

There is one other component in this circuit whose function hasn't been described. This is the by-pass capacitor, C_3. As you know, the output signal from this amplifier is produced by fluctuations in the current passing through the load resistor, R_1. But the same current fluctuations occur in the emitter resistor, R_2. Fortunately, R_2 is very small compared to R_1, so a current fluctuation that produces a 4 V change in R_1 produces only about a 4 mV change across R_2. Still, even this 4 mV change tends to reduce the gain of the amplifier. This is because the 4 mV voltage is in phase with the incoming signal and thus reduces the bias change by 4 mV. Remember that the peak signal voltage of .02 V caused a change of this amount in forward bias. However, if the emitter voltage also changes in the same direction by 4 mV, the net change in bias falls from .02 V to .02 − .004, which equals .016 V.

This loss is prevented by the by-pass capacitor, which acts as a sort of "shock absorber," flattening out the fluctuations in voltage at the emitter. In this way, it holds the emitter voltage constant. As a result, the gain of the amplifier is not degraded. Some amplifier designers don't find this component necessary; therefore, amplifiers may be made without a by-pass capacitor.

Notice that, in this amplifier, only the emitter voltage is not fluctuated by the audio signal. The base voltage is fluctuated by the incoming signal, and the output signal is produced by fluctuations in the collector voltage. The emitter voltage does not fluctuate. This remains constant and acts as a common reference point to the audio signal; hence, its name—*common emitter* configuration. The characteristics of this type of amplifier are as follows:

Common Emitter Amplifier Characteristics

Input impedance	Moderate (500 Ω to 12 kΩ)
Output impedance	Moderate (12 kΩ to 50 kΩ)
Current gain (= I_c/I_B)	Moderate
Voltage gain	Moderate
Power gain	Moderate
Phase reversal	

It follows from these characteristics that the common emitter can be used for general purpose amplification, because it gives moderate amplification of both voltage and power. It can also be used as a middle stage in amplifying low to medium power signals in a signal generator or other signal processing equipment.

Common Base Amplifiers

The circuit diagram of a typical NPN common base amplifier is shown in Figure 7-10. The theory of operation for this amplifier is similar to that for the common emitter configuration. In all of these amplifiers, R_3 and R_4 act as a voltage divider, producing the required forward bias at the base. Also, C_1 and C_2 are coupling capacitors, passing the AC audio signal and blocking the DC.

The only difference between the common base and common emitter is that, in the common base circuit, the incoming signal fluctuates the emitter voltage instead of the base voltage. Thus, in this configuration, the signal fluctuates the forward bias by bringing the emitter voltage closer or farther from the base voltage, instead of bringing the base voltage closer or farther from the emitter voltage. The result is that, in the first half-cycle, when the input signal is positive,

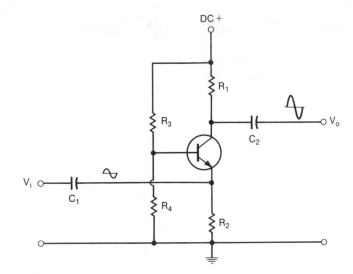

Fig. 7-10
Common base
amplifier

the bias voltage is reduced (V_E being closer to V_B instead of farther from it), and in the second half-cycle, the bias voltage is increased. This phase difference produces an output signal that is not phase inverted. It is in phase with the incoming signal. Also, because now the input current to the transistor is not the leakage current from the base, but the emitter current, there can be no current gain. In fact, there is a slight current loss, because all current that enters at the emitter ($I_E = I_C + I_B$), and, since $I_C = I_E - I_B$, then the output current, I_C, must be less than the input current. However, due to the fact that R_2 is less in value than R_1, there is a large voltage gain. The characteristics of this configuration are as follows:

Common Base Amplifier Characteristics

Input impedance	Low (30 Ω to 150 Ω)
Output impedance	High (750 Ω to 1 MΩ)
Current gain (= I_C/I_E)	Less than unity
Voltage gain	High
Power gain	Moderate
No phase reversal	

Because of its extremely high voltage gain, this type of amplifier can be used in the first stage of a pre-amplifier, where very low voltage signals require large voltage amplification. The low input impedance can accept a signal from a low impedance line or microphone, but some voltage loss occurs. The high output impedance can be coupled to a high input impedance following stage; however, because of the disadvantage of such a high output impedance and the difficulty of correct impedance matching, this type of amplifier is not often used.

Common Collector Amplifiers

This configuration is often called an *emitter follower*. The circuit configuration of an NPN common collector is shown in Figure 7-11.

Fig. 7-11
Common collector
(emitter follower)
amplifier

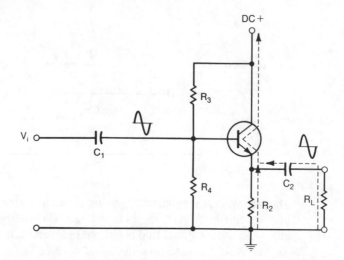

In this circuit, R_3 and R_4, as well as C_1 and C_2, fulfill the same functions as they did in the two previous circuits. Notice that in the common emitter circuit, the emitter voltage remained constant. In the common base circuit, the base voltage remained constant. So also in the common collector circuit, the collector voltage remains constant, acting as a fixed reference that is common to the incoming and outgoing signal. As before, the fluctuating voltage at the base fluctuates the bias, and in so doing, fluctuates the current through the transistor.

The most striking difference between this circuit and the previous circuits is that there is no load resistor, R_1, here. The reason is that the output is taken from the emitter. It is not the output voltage, but the output current that is important. For this reason I have included the load, R_L; the dotted lines show the current through the transistor, which flows partly through R_L and partly through R_2. This fluctuating current, flowing in the voice coil of a loudspeaker, forms the powerful output from this circuit, which drives the speakers and produces the sound.

Common Collector Amplifier Characteristics

Input impedance	High (10 kΩ to 500 kΩ)
Output impedance	Low (0.5 Ω to 100 Ω)
Current gain (= I_E/I_B)	High
Voltage gain	Less than unity
Power gain	High
No phase reversal	

Notice that the voltage gain is less than unity. This is because the output voltage at the emitter is in phase with the input voltage at the base. However, change of bias depends on the difference between these two, and unity gain requires that they be equal. This is impossible, because the change in V_B must be greater than that in V_E to produce bias change and activate the amplifier. Therefore, voltage gain is always just less than unity in this circuit configuration.

In the absence of voltage gain, all gain occurs as current gain. For this reason, system designers use this circuit as the output stage of all power amplifiers. At this end of the audio chain, the *driver* amplifier has already raised the signal voltage to about 8 or more volts, so voltage gain is no longer needed. What is needed is power gain. As you know, power can be calculated from the product of current and voltage. Because the signal voltage is substantially the same at the input and output of this amplifier, the power gain is roughly proportional to the current gain. This is what is needed to drive a low impedance loudspeaker, so this amplifier configuration is used to drive loudspeakers or other equipment where powerful electrical signals are needed.

One output transistor might not have sufficient current gain to provide the power needed by a loudspeaker system. However, there is a method of combining two transistors in the common collector configuration that provides extremely high current gain. This arrangement is called a *Darlington pair*. The two transistors can be separate or incorporated in a single package called a *Darlington transistor*. The connections and current paths are shown in Figure 7-12.

Fig. 7-12
Darlington
transistor

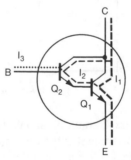

I have labeled the two transistors Q_1 and Q_2. Assuming that these are silicon transistors, the required bias between the E and B terminals is 1.2 V (0.6 V for each transistor). It is the change in this bias voltage that controls the current, just as in a single transistor.

The output current, I_1, is a multiple of a small leakage current, I_2, from the Q_1 base. But I_2 acts as the main current through Q_2. This, in turn, is associated with an even smaller leakage current, I_3, through the Q_2 base terminal.

Assume that the current gain of Q_2 is 40, and that the gain of Q_1 is 30. Then the total current gain is 40×30, which equals 1,200. This is such a useful arrangement that a Darlington pair is almost invariably used at the output of a power amplifier.

Class A Amplifiers

The class of an amplifier depends only on the bias point of its active component. As can be seen from the current/voltage graph in Figure 7-13, the current conducted by a transistor is linearly proportional to the bias voltage above the cutoff point. This straight line proportionality stretches from cutoff to saturation. Notice that class B amplifiers are biased exactly at cutoff point. But more about class B amplifiers later.

Fig. 7-13
Transistor
characteristic
curve

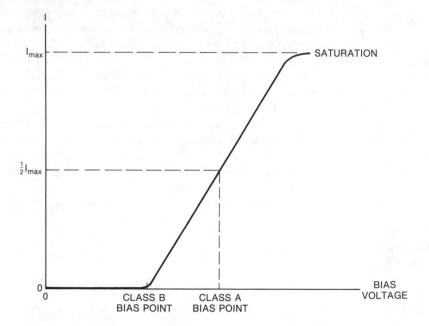

A class A amplifier should be biased half-way along the straight portion of its slope. The transistor then conducts half of its maximum current. The effect of an input signal is to fluctuate the bias voltage; it can be seen from Figure 7-14A that this causes similar fluctuations in the current output. The disadvantages of wrong bias voltage can be seen from Figure 7-14B and C.

Because half of the maximum current flows through the transistor at all times, this class of amplifier is energy inefficient. In amplifier stages where very little power is used, such as in pre-amplifier and line amplifier stages, this offers no problem. In the output stage of a power amplifier, however, large amounts of current are used, so this energy inefficiency causes power supply and cooling problems. Consequently, it is not often that a class A output stage is found in a power amplifier. Designers look for a more energy efficient amplifier classification. This can be found in the class B amplifier.

Fig. 7-14 Effects of bias voltage in a class A amplifier

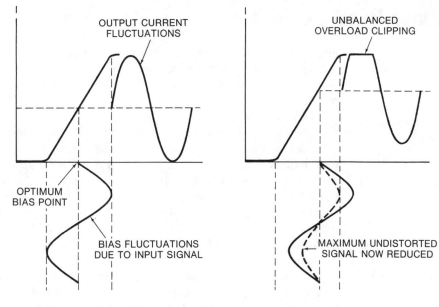

OUTPUT CURRENT FLUCTUATIONS

OPTIMUM BIAS POINT

BIAS FLUCTUATIONS DUE TO INPUT SIGNAL

(A) Optimum class A bias—gives maximum undistorted output by using the full current range of the transistor from zero to saturation.

UNBALANCED OVERLOAD CLIPPING

MAXIMUM UNDISTORTED SIGNAL NOW REDUCED

(B) Bias voltage too high—half-wave overload clipping due to saturation

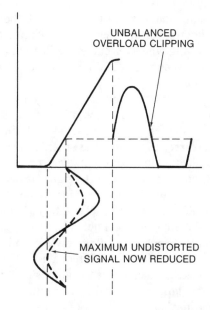

UNBALANCED OVERLOAD CLIPPING

MAXIMUM UNDISTORTED SIGNAL NOW REDUCED

(C) Bias voltage too low—half-wave overload clipping due to cutoff

Class B Amplifiers

Figure 7-13 shows that this class of amplifier is biased exactly at cutoff point, so it appears to conduct only the positive half of an audio signal. During the negative half-cycle, the bias voltage falls below cutoff, so there is no second half-cycle response.

This problem can be solved by feeding the signal into two complementary polarized transistors, namely an NPN and a PNP. The result is that voltage moving in the forward bias direction for one transistor moves in the reverse bias direction for the other. Let us call the transistors *A* and *B*. This arrangement ensures that while *A* is conducting, *B* is cut off. And while *B* is conducting, *A* is cut off. The transistors are then said to be in push-pull. However, special arrangements have to be made to bias each transistor at cutoff point, because *A* (if a silicon NPN) requires $+0.6$ V, and *B* (a silicon PNP) requires -0.6 V of bias. The problem is how to maintain this differential voltage of 1.2 V between the inputs of the two transistors.

One simple way to achieve this is to use a direct coupled class A *driver stage*. This feeds the signal to the bases of the two complementary output transistors. By including two silicon diodes between the complementary inputs, the two voltages are held 1.2 V apart (see Figure 7-15).

The 1.2 V differential voltage results from the barrier potential (which numerically equals the cutoff voltage) of the two diodes. Because the class A driver, Q_1, ensures that current flows through these diodes at all times, there is always this differential of 1.2 V across the diodes. Also, because this voltage remains virtually constant, whatever current is flowing (unlike the voltage across a resistor), there remains only a DC component between the signal inputs, as can be seen from Figure 7-16.

The shaded area illustrates which part of the signal each transistor is conducting. The rest of the time, its bias has fallen below cutoff. The complete signal is reconstituted in the loudspeaker. Here the current alternates as it flows, first in one direction, then in the other. You could say that while the signal is positive, Q_2 conducts, and the current (electron flow) flows through the loudspeaker and Q_2 to DC positive $(+)$; while the signal is negative, current flows from the DC negative $(-)$ through Q_3 and the loudspeaker to ground.

Returning to the schematic of Figure 7-15, the three branch currents (shown by dotted lines) are labeled I_0, I_1, and I_2. I_0 is a very small current that enables R_2 and R_3 to act as a voltage divider and produce the required quiescent voltage at the base of Q_1. I_1 is a larger current. Its fluctuations produce the output signal across R_1, which forms the input signal to the next stage. This, in turn, produces a much larger fluctuating current, I_2, through Q_2 and Q_3, which powers the loudspeaker.

With an understanding of the principles behind semiconductors, construction of simple amplifiers can be undertaken, from which useful additional experience

Fig. 7-15
Complementary
class B output
stage fed by a
direct coupled
class A driver

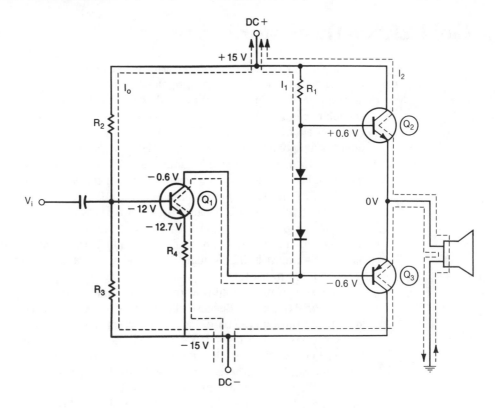

Fig. 7-16
Differentially
biased audio
signal inputs
feeding a
complementary
class B output
transistor

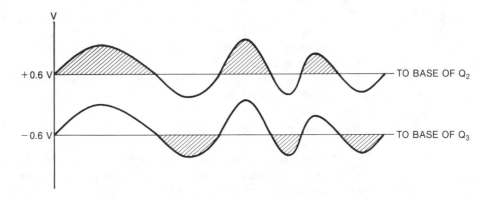

can be gained. But more importantly, basic troubleshooting and maintenance can be undertaken with an understanding of the working principles behind amplifiers. This is far more satisfactory than relying on other people to maintain equipment in good condition and make basic repairs.

Field Effect Transistors

A completely different type of transistor is becoming commonly used to meet the increasing demand for improved signal-to-noise ratio brought about by the advent of digital audio. This is a unipolar device called a *field effect transistor* (FET). Unipolar refers to the fact that the current flows entirely through a single doped medium, either an N-doped channel or a P-doped channed. In this case, a single polarity (unipolar) conductor is used, whereas in a conventional transistor, current has to negotiate two PN junctions and flow through both N- and P-type material. For this reason, a conventional transistor is referred to as bipolar.

The FET has two main advantages over a bipolar transistor. It produces less background noise. This is because the electron flow through a PN junction causes much of the noise in a bipolar transistor. Also, the FET has far greater input impedance. In the form of an insulated gate FET, the input impedance is as high as 15 MΩ—almost infinitely high—so there is no leakage current, as is the case with a bipolar transistor.

It has been mentioned that the bias voltage controls the current through a conventional transistor. Because about 2 percent of the collector current is always leaking out through the base, the main current flow becomes proportional to the leakage current. The bipolar transistor is, therefore, called a *current controlled device*. Because there is virtually no current leakage from a FET, this unipolar transistor can be considered a voltage controlled device.

The disadvantage of a FET compared to a conventional transistor is that it can handle less current than a power transistor. However, in a pre-amplifier, where current flow is small anyway and low background noise is at a premium, FETs are ideally suitable, and a FET pre-amplifier or op-amp is preferable to a bipolar transistorized product.

The theory behind the operation of a FET is as follows. The structure consists basically of a single doped channel surrounded by a sleeve of oppositely doped material. The ends of the channel are called the *source* (where the current enters) and the *drain* (where the current leaves). The surrounding sleeve is called the *gate*. This controls the amount of current that can flow through the channel. The basic structure is illustrated in Figure 7-17A and B, and the corresponding schematic symbols in Figure 7-17C and D.

Notice that the direction of the arrow in the schematic symbol indicates whether the channel is N or P. As ever, the arrow indicates the direction of conventional current flow (holes flow) across a junction. Between the gate and channel in Figure 7-17C, forward bias would occur if the gate (P material) were more positive than the N channel. So, the inward pointing arrow signifies that the channel is N. Similarly, the outward pointing arrow in Figure 7-17D indicates a P channel.

If no voltage were applied to the gate, the channel would conduct current with practically no resistance, so maximum current flows when there is no bias voltage. (Bias voltage is the voltage between the source and gate, V_{SG}.) Voltage in

Fig. 7-17 J-FETs

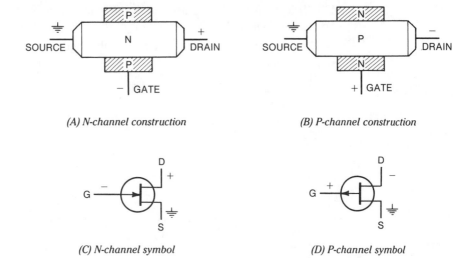

(A) N-channel construction   *(B) P-channel construction*

(C) N-channel symbol   *(D) P-channel symbol*

the same polarity as from S to D is considered forward bias; therefore, a voltage at the gate that is more negative than the source has to be applied in an N-channel FET to limit the current flow. The polarities required for correct functioning are shown in Figure 7-17.

Let us consider the action of an N-channel FET to see how the current can be controlled by a reverse bias voltage at the gate. As you know, a depletion zone, where majority current carriers have been cancelled, occurs spontaneously at a PN junction. (See the first section in this chapter.) By applying a negative voltage to the gate of an N-channel FET, the negative field extends farther into the channel than the extent of the normal depletion zone. This negative field repels any free N current carriers and has the effect of increasing the depletion zone by expelling negative carriers. This reduces the effective size of the channel through which current can flow.

The greater the negative voltage applied to the gate, the farther the negative field extends into the channel, reducing the channel size even more. If enough negative voltage is applied, the N channel can be pinched off by the expanding negative field effect. This completely cuts off all current flow from source to drain. The gate voltage that entirely cuts off current is called the *pinch-off* voltage, as opposed to the *cutoff* voltage in a bipolar transistor (see Figure 7-18).

These FETs, in which the gate is in contact with the channel, are called *junction FETs* (J-FETs) to distinguish them from *insulated gate* FETs, which will be discussed later. The characteristics of J-FETs are

- The J-FET conducts maximum current when no bias is applied.
- Reverse bias applied to the gate controls the current by reducing the channel size, due to an electrical field that extends from the gate into the channel.

- If sufficient reverse bias is applied to the gate, the current channel can be completely pinched off by the extent of the electrical field.

- J-FETs are a type of *depletion* FET, so called because the effect of bias is to deplete the current carriers and reduce channel conduction accordingly.

Fig. 7-18 Effects of negative voltage applied to the gate

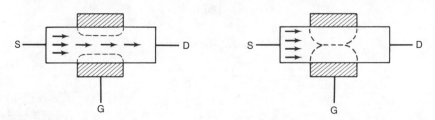

(A) Field produced by reverse bias reduces channel width and restricts current.   *(B) Field pinches off all current when reverse bias reaches pinch-off level.*

J-FETs work extremely well under reverse bias conditions. As long as their circuitry never requires them to withstand forward bias, there is no problem. But there are occasions in which an overload or some other situation could forward bias a J-FET. If this should happen, it would cause serious trouble, because no measurable current should flow from the gate into the channel. When the J-FET is reverse biased, this cannot happen. But if the FET should become forward biased, the gate/channel junction would also be forward biased and it would conduct a large amount of current.

To deal with this problem, an insulated gate FET was developed. The insulation between the gate and channel must be very thin, so that the electrical field from the gate can penetrate the channel to a sufficient depth. This insulation layer is, in practice, created by plating a thin film of nonconducting metal oxide onto the inside of the channel. This is called a *metal-oxide semiconductor field effect transistor* (MOSFET).

This layer of insulation has to be so thin that even the static charge on a person's finger or the tip of a soldering iron can break it down. This would destroy the transistor. To avoid this, the operator is advised not to touch the gate. A soldering iron should have a flexible jumper connected by an alligator clip cable between the tip and a convenient ground during soldering.

There are several advantages to using MOSFETs instead of J-FETs. The first, already mentioned, is that a temporary reversal of bias will not cause current to flow from the channel through the gate. The other advantage is that a completely new family of FETs can now be created, because it becomes possible to use forward bias without unfortunate consequences. This new family of FETS, called *enhancement* MOSFETs, is shown in Figure 7-19.

Let us consider an N-channel enhancement MOSFET (a P channel works the same way, but with reversed polarities), as in Figure 7-19. The structure of an enhancement MOSFET can be viewed as having the gate on one side of the channel and a substrate on the other. This substrate is heavily doped with P-type

Fig. 7-19
Enhancement
MOSFETs

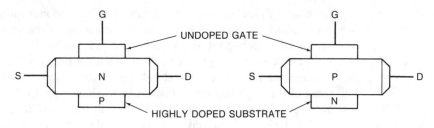

(A) Structure

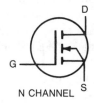 

(B) Schematic symbols

Fig. 7-20
Summary of field
effect transistors

 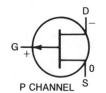

(A) J-FETs (Depletion type—reverse bias reduces current.)

(B) MOSFETS (Depletion type—reverse bias reduces current.)

 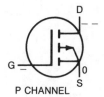

(C) MOSFETs (Enhancement type—forward bias increases current.)

material. Its junction with the channel (a PN junction) produces a large depletion zone, which extends right across the channel to the gate. So the channel is completely pinched off, even when no bias is applied.

The gate is not doped at all. When forward biased with a positive voltage, the gate emits a positive electrical field that extends into the channel. This reverses some of the depletion effect caused by the substrate, and effectively repels some of the positive current carriers from the substrate that have neutralized N carriers in the N channel. In this way, the positive field from the gate enhances the number of free current carriers. This enables current to be conducted. The greater the forward bias, the greater the amount of current that flows. The substrate is usually internally connected to the source. It is not the voltage of the substrate, but its doping that enables it to produce the required depletion effect.

To summarize, an enhancement MOSFET conducts no current when unbiased. When forward bias is applied to the gate, current flows in proportion to the bias, up to saturation point. A summary of the different types of FETs and their modes of action is given in Figure 7-20.

8 The Tape Recorder

8 The Tape Recorder

Tape Recording Concepts

Surely one of the greatest achievements of mankind has been the ability to record and reproduce sound with clarity and fidelity. Perhaps the most useful and versatile mechanism for doing this is the tape recorder. Practically everybody uses a tape recorder, but not many have the ability to use one to obtain top quality sound recording and reproduction. Detailed technical knowledge and an understanding of the principles underlying magnetic recording are necessary to achieve this quality.

It is not necessary to be a professional studio engineer, nor is it necessary to use the most expensive studio equipment. What is necessary is to use a well manufactured consumer product and, above all, to understand thoroughly how it functions and how best to utilize its abilities and limitations.

All equipment has limitations. The competent operator knows what those limitations are and adjusts his/her activities accordingly. For example, it is possible to overload a recording. Too high a recording level produces overload distortion of the amplitude peaks. Too low a recording level definitely avoids this problem, but then the quiet passages become lost in background noise. Adjusting the sound level within the parameters of the dynamic range available, as indicated by the recording level meter, can avoid both causes of sound degradation.

Manufacturers are well aware of the comparative incompetence of many tape recorder users and they cater to this market, so they have to try to make their equipment as "idiot proof" as possible. To do this, they often incorporate a built-in automatic level control. This acts as a limiter and avoids overload distortion by automatically attenuating peak signals. But it reduces the dynamic range available, so it produces, at best, a second-rate recording. The knowledgeable recording operator avoids using this built-in device whenever possible and relies on his/her regulation of the recording level to obtain the best possible recording results. The requirement, then, is to understand the theory and practice of tape recording. And the first requirement is to understand the theoretical principles behind magnetic recording.

Theory of Operation

Before going into a detailed description of how sound is magnetically recorded onto tape, I need to mention the *domain* theory of magnetism. This theory postulates that the molecular structure of iron (or other permeable material) contains a large number of domains. Each domain behaves as a very small bar magnet, with its own north and south pole. Normally, the domains are arranged in a haphazard manner, so that the individual polarities cancel out. Figure 8-1 shows these domains in (A) an unmagnetized, (B) a partially magnetized, and (C) a fully magnetized state.

Fig. 8-1 Magnetic domains

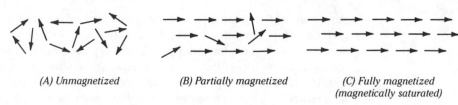

(A) Unmagnetized   (B) Partially magnetized   (C) Fully magnetized
                                                             (magnetically saturated)

When a strong magnetizing force, in the form of a magnetic field, is applied to this material, it reorients the domains so that they cease to be haphazard and start to align themselves in the direction of the magnetic field. This causes the material to become magnetized. The degree of magnetization is determined by the proportion of domains that become aligned to those that remain haphazard.

The magnetic tape used in tape recording consists of a layer of permeable material (basically iron oxide) deposited evenly onto a flexible tape base. The iron oxide contains multitudes of domains. Those that come under the influence of a magnetic field become magnetized. That is, they become polarized in one direction or another depending on the direction of the applied field. If the N pole is to their right and the S pole is to their left, the domains become oriented with their S poles to the right and their N poles to the left. If the applied field is reversed, the domains also reverse their polarity. This is basically what happens when sound is recorded onto magnetic tape.

The tape head consists of a small horseshoe piece of permeable material. Think of it as soft iron that can easily be magnetized in one direction or the other. A coil of thin insulated wire is wound around it, and as a current is passed through this coil, the iron turns into an electromagnet, creating a strong magnetic field in the air gap between its poles. If the current is reversed, the polarity of the field is reversed. In fact, the field fluctuates in strength and polarity in exact proportion to the current in the coil.

In a tape recorder, the audio signal runs through the coil that energizes the record head and produces in its air gap a fluctuating magnetic field that is precisely proportional to the audio signal. Meanwhile, the tape is passing over the head at constant speed, so the magnetic imprint on the tape exactly corresponds to the instantaneous value of the audio signal at all times. This can best be seen by an illustration of one full sound wave cycle, as shown in Figure 8-2.

Notice that as the polarity of the current flowing through the head reverses, so the polarity of the magnetization imprinted on the tape also reverses. In this way, the signal voltage is magnetically recorded onto the tape so that its intensity and polarity exactly parallel the audio signal current.

When it is necessary to reproduce this recording, the tape is rewound and the connections from the head are reassigned to the pre-amplifier of the reproduce system. During playback, the tape is again transported past the head at constant speed. But now the magnetized domains on the tape produce the fluctuating magnetic field in the air gap between the poles of the tape head. It is interesting to note that the process of electromagnetism is reversible. Just as a fluctuating current in the head produces a fluctuating magnetic field in the air gap, so, during reproduction, a fluctuating magnetic field in the air gap produces a fluctuating current in the head coil. True, this is a very small current. But it is applied through a head pre-amplifier, amplified again in the reproduce amplifier, and then passed to a power amplifier, which drives the speakers.

To summarize, during the recording process, the audio signal is applied to the coil of the tape head. This magnetizes the tape as it passes over the head, with a polarity and intensity that exactly parallel the value of the audio signal voltage, both in amplitude and frequency. During reproduction, the strength and polarity of the magnetic recording on the tape produce a fluctuating magnetic field across the tape head, so that the induced current in the head coil exactly parallels the magnetic field in amplitude, polarity, and frequency.

This sounds very simple. In essence it is. And, as you know, it works. But when this new invention of magnetic recording was first being developed, some very serious problems had to be solved. These problems and the solutions that were eventually found to overcome them, are discussed in the next section.

Mechanical and Electrical Requirements

A tape recorder (and its more sophisticated version, the video recorder) is a combined product of mechanical and electronic engineering. The mechanical parts of the system have to produce a tape transport mechanism that can move the tape past the head at precisely constant speed while holding it in vertical

Fig. 8-2 Magnetic
recording of a full
sound wave cycle

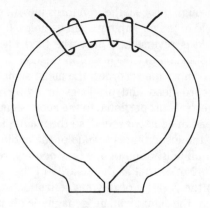

(A) Plan view of head

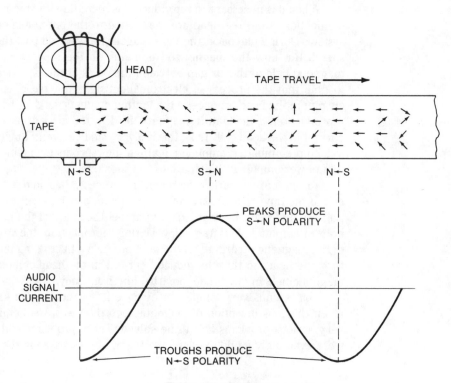

(B) Magnetic recording process

alignment with the head. It must also be able to either fast forward or fast rewind
the tape when required. It must be able to maintain tape tension within limits that
do not stretch or break the tape. In addition, the mechanical construction of the
head must fulfill many exacting demands that will be discussed later.

Electromagnetic Requirements

Perhaps the most difficult problem that first had to be overcome was electromagnetic. The previous section described how the magnetic imprint on the tape had to parallel the signal current passing through the record head exactly. But in fact, when this method of magnetic recording was first tried, this linear relationship between magnetization and head current did not take place. There was extreme distortion, which, if uncorrected, would have made magnetic recording impractical.

The problem was related to what could be thought of as internal static resistance to the movement of domains when a reversal of magnetization was initiated. It was a form of magnetic hysteresis. Hysteresis is described in the appendix at the end of this book, but briefly, it appears that once the process of magnetization is under way, it continues in proportion to the magnetizing force. However, as soon as there is a reversal of the magnetizing force, a response lag occurs. The result is that a considerable change of magnetizing force has to take place before any corresponding demagnetization occurs. This is what causes distortion at the peaks of the waveform. And this is what, at first, seemed to make the dream of magnetic sound recording unobtainable.

This static internal friction, which opposes the initial process of reversal, can best be illustrated by an analogy. If iron filings are sprinkled onto a piece of paper and a magnet is placed beneath the paper, the filings move into a pattern, aligning themselves with the magnetic lines of force. If the magnet is slowly moved, the filings do not move at first. Eventually, however, they start to move and from then on continue to follow the motion of the magnet. If the magnet reverses direction, there is another lag in the movement of the filings. This occurs at every reversal of motion. It is due to static friction between the filings and the paper.

The problem in magnetic sound recording is how to make the domains respond without a time lag at the points of magnetic reversal, which is at the wave peaks. To continue with our analogy, the problem boils down to making the iron filings respond instantly, without any delay due to static friction, when the magnet starts to reverse its direction.

If, as a possible solution, the paper is jiggled rapidly up and down, so that the filings are always in motion, they continue to align themselves in accordance with the magnetic field lines as they fall. However, in this situation, there is no delay in their response to a reversal of motion as the magnet starts to reverse its direction. This is because the filings are freed from static friction by the up and down motion produced by the jiggling.

What could be used in magnetic recording that corresponds to this jiggling of the iron filings? The superimposing of a high-frequency, ultrasonic signal onto the audio signal was found to be the answer. This superimposed frequency, applied during the recording process, is called *bias voltage*. It is always AC and ultrasonic; in fact, it is usually between 80 and 200 kHz. It can be filtered out during reproduction by a bias trap (a sharp cutoff stopband filter). What is left is a perfect, undistorted magnetic recording, which can be reproduced with perfect fidelity. The optimum bias voltage to be used depends on the characteristics of the recording tape, and to a slight extent, on the preference of the recording engineer. A method for determining a suitable bias voltage is described later.

Record/Reproduce Head Requirements

The construction of the record/reproduce head was also a limiting factor in the performance of early tape recorders. The problem was in achieving a narrow enough head gap so that the full range of audible frequencies could be recorded. It was easy to record the lower and mid frequencies, but the highest frequencies were a problem. That is because there is a definite relationship between the highest recordable frequency and the width of the head gap. The higher the frequency, the narrower the air gap has to be, or alternatively, the faster the tape speed has to be, or both.

In the early days, high tape speeds of $7\frac{1}{2}$ or 15 ips were necessary. Even then, frequencies could be recorded only up to about 6 kHz. Manufacturing techniques have since improved. Cassette recorders, running at $1\frac{7}{8}$ ips, can now record up to 16 kHz, an octave higher than could formerly be recorded at $7\frac{1}{2}$ ips.

The reason why head gap, tape speed, and maximum frequency are interrelated results from the wavelength occupied by each sound cycle. Remember that tape runs at a constant speed; therefore, low frequencies of, say, 20 Hz produce 20 cycles (or waves) in the length of tape that runs in 1 second. At a speed of $7\frac{1}{2}$ ips, a length of $7\frac{1}{2}/20$ inches is occupied by each cycle. This is a 0.375-inch wavelength. The head gap has to be not more than half this wavelength, so that the positive half-cycle and negative half-cycle are not included in the head gap at the same time. If they were, they would cancel each other out.

At this tape speed of $7\frac{1}{2}$ ips, the maximum size of head gap can be calculated for the most difficult situation, which occurs at the highest frequency. For good results, a recorder should record up to 15 kHz. At a tape speed of $7\frac{1}{2}$ ips, 15,000 cycles occupy a tape length of $7\frac{1}{2}$ inches. So 1 cycle occupies a wavelength on tape of $7\frac{1}{2}/15000$, which is 0.5 mil—that is, 0.5 of a thousandth of an inch. Because the head gap must be not more than half this length, a head gap of 0.25 mil is needed. In fact, most audio heads for this tape speed are made with a 0.2-mil gap. However, at 15 ips, the wavelength occupied is twice as long (twice as much tape having passed during this time period), so this same head can record up to 30 kHz (twice the frequency), other factors being equal.

Now consider how narrow the gap must be on a cassette recorder in which the tape speed is only $1\frac{7}{8}$ ips. This must record 15,000 cycles in a length of $1\frac{7}{8}$ inches. So each cycle, each wavelength, is 1.875/15000, which is 0.125 mil. But the head gap must be less than half this amount, so the head has to be ground to a gap width of 62.5 microinches.

Other factors that have to be accommodated in tape head construction include such things as use of highly permeable material that can respond readily to the magnetizing field. Also, hardness is required to resist premature wear resulting from the friction of the tape. Unfortunately, these two requirements tend to be mutually opposed. But special ferrite materials are being used for tape head construction, which give long hours of use with acceptable permeability. Head wear is a factor for which the recording engineer must be alert. Once a tape head wears past a certain point, the high-frequency response falls off sharply. Regular frequency response tests with a test tape are needed to ensure that the recorder continues to operate satisfactorily. Loss of HF could indicate head failure due to wear.

The reason why HF loss occurs due to wear is that wear tends to increase the width of the head gap. One of the telltale signs to watch out for (you cannot see the head gap; it is too small) is on the face plate surrounding the head. If the tape has worn this down so that it has channeled out a recess for itself, with shoulders above and below the tape path, then you can be sure that the tape has eaten into the head by the same amount.

It is also necessary to keep the head clean. Any accumulation of dirt on the surface of the head(s) has a disastrous effect on the high-frequency response. The reason is that dirt has the effect of lifting the tape away from the head surface. This enables the magnetic field to spread out on each side of the head gap before it reaches the tape. Thus, it effectively widens the head gap. It has already been shown that any widening of the head gap reduces the high-frequency response.

Tape Transport Requirements

Another requirement of the mechanical tape transport system is that the tape pass the head at precisely constant speed. Because no electromechanical system is perfect, there are bound to be slight fluctuations in the friction and motor torque, so special precautions have to be taken to even out any resulting speed variations. The main precaution is the provision of a heavy, smooth-running flywheel attached to the capstan motor shaft. The rapid rotation of this flywheel evens out most of the inevitable speed fluctuations by virtue of its rotational inertia.

It should be understood that the tape speed is entirely determined by the capstan motor, which drives the capstan. During the record and reproduce modes of operation, the tape is held tightly against this capstan by a rubber *pinch roller*. This prevents any tape slip between the capstan and the tape. So the tape speed is the same as the speed at which the circumference of the capstan is moving. Through the use of an accurately speed-controlled capstan motor and heavy flywheel, speed is held as constant as possible. Remember that the take-up motor and rewind motor should not affect the tape speed in any way during the record or reproduce modes. They affect the tape speed only during fast forward and fast rewind, when the tape is out of contact with the capstan and the heads.

During the record and reproduce modes, there is a very slight torque from both the rewind motor and the take-up motor. This slight torque is merely to prevent any slack between the supply reel and the heads, and to take up the slack as the tape leaves the capstan (so that it doesn't accumulate on the floor). Test this out. During playback, stop the take-up reel by hand. You will see that the tape continues to pass the heads at the same speed due to the action of the capstan and pinch roller. Some unwound tape will then start to accumulate. Stop the recorder and wind up the slack by hand. Don't just let go, or the rapid winding of the take-up reel might stretch or break the tape when the end of the slack has been reached.

Any fault in this constant speed system usually manifests itself as what is called *wow* or *flutter*. By playing a constant mid-frequency note from a test tape, it is easy to hear the effect of any speed fluctuations. A fairly slow, cyclical rise and fall in the speed sounds like a repeated "wow, wow" superimposed on the sound. This can be caused by a fault in the capstan motor, producing a cyclical fluctuation in motor speed. It can also be caused by excessive take-up torque produced by the take-up motor; or by friction, as bent and pinched flanges on the take-up reel catch on the tape at each revolution and cause intermittent tape slip past the capstan.

Try holding the take-up reel stationary for a few seconds and see if this cures the problem. If it does, you have the cause. The trouble might also come from the supply reel. To find out, try unwinding a few feet of tape; then, holding the supply reel stationary, play back the slack tape. If that cures the problem, the fault was connected with the supply reel. If neither of these are at fault, examine the capstan, pinch roller, and capstan motor for problems.

The other audible effect of unsteady speed is called *flutter*. This is a rapid cyclical fluctuation of speed, which sounds like a flutter superimposed on the sound. It is often caused by an accumulation of dirt (usually magnetic coating from the tape) adhering to the capstan. This lump of dirt produces a slight eccentricity in the radius of the capstan. Because this is rotating at constant speed, the intermittent excess radius causes the tape to speed up momentarily every time that piece of dirt inserts itself between the capstan and tape (once per revolution). This problem is easily cured by cleaning the capstan and pinch roller with denatured alcohol on the end of a cotton swab. This should be done regularly whenever the heads are cleaned.

In portable recorders, the speed regulation of the capstan motor is often achieved by an electromechanical governor. In line-powered machines, it may be achieved by using a synchronous motor. Synchronous motor speeds are automatically linked to the AC line frequency that powers them. Variable speeds can be obtained by using a power amplified signal-generator output to drive the capstan synchronous motor. The oscillator frequency can then be used to control the tape speed (within limits). However, digital logic is taking over where electromechanical systems used to be employed.

Digital control of tape speed can be achieved quite simply. A multitoothed wheel is included on the capstan drive shaft. A narrow beam of light is directed through this toothed wheel onto a photosensitive cell, whose output goes to a digital counter. At each sample period (which may be every half-second or so), the number of teeth interrupting the light beam is digitally counted. This count is then compared, using a *greater than/less than* comparator, to a binary number stored in ROM (read only memory), which is incorporated by the manufacturers. The ROM has stored in its memory the exact required number of teeth that should pass the light beam during one sample period, assuming correct tape speed. The output of the comparator indicates if the recorder is running too fast or too slow, and a speed adjustment is automatically made until the two numbers coincide. This test is carried out every half-second or so, depending on the sampling frequency. It ensures extremely accurate speed control, and it can also be linked to other compatible timing systems to synchronize two or more recorders.

Internal Equalization

The equalization and alignment routine needed for good quality recording is described in Chapter 11. Before we are ready for that, however, it is necessary to say something about the record and reproduce equalization already built into the tape machine. It is generally accepted that bass notes tend to become lost in background noise, and also that, during recording, the high frequencies become attenuated due to the bias voltage. Bias, as you know, is necessary to avoid distortion. It also helps to reduce background noise. But the fact is that it somewhat attenuates the high frequencies. The greater the applied bias, the more attenuation of high frequencies there is.

To counteract these losses, the record amplifier contains an equalization filter that slightly boosts the low frequencies and considerably boosts the high frequencies. This boosting of the signal before recording is called *pre-emphasis*. The bass boosting is intended to be cancelled by an equal bass cut during reproduction. Its only purpose is to reduce noise. The high-frequency boosting is necessary to counteract losses.

During playback, an equalization filter is incorporated in the reproduce amplifier. This reproduce filtering is called *post-emphasis*. It is needed to counteract the bass boost supplied during recording, and again to boost the high frequencies to counteract new losses. In order for recording to be compatible on all machines, the post-emphasis filter has been standardized. In this country, it is called the NAB Standard Reproducing Characteristic. (NAB stands for the National Association of Broadcasters.) In Europe, there is a slightly different post-emphasis standard. It is called the CCIR Reproducing Characteristic. (CCIR stands for Consultative Committee for International Radio.) Its main difference is that there is no bass cut of 10 dB at 30 Hz.

There is one other important filter added to the post-emphasis network. Called an *integration filter*, it acts as a pole that boosts the low frequencies by 6 dB/octave at each lower octave below 15 kHz. This is needed because the output from the reproduce head falls off by 6 dB at each lower octave as the frequency falls.

Remember that the head gap is designed to equal half the wavelength of the signal at 15 kHz. At each lower octave (when the frequency is halved), only half of the correspondingly longer wave is contained within the head gap, so the signal amplitude falls by half (6 dB). You can also look at it this way: In the inductor that forms the head, it is the rate of change of magnetic flux that induces the voltage. Lower frequencies become flatter as their wavelengths extend, so the slope (rate of change) reduces in proportion to the reduction of frequency.

To summarize, during recording, there is a pre-emphasis of the signal, which boosts the low and high frequencies. During reproduce, there is a post-emphasis consisting of two filters. One is the NAB filter, which cuts the low and again boosts the high frequencies. The other acts as a pole and boosts the low frequencies to counteract the reduced response of the head as the frequency falls. The result of all this filtering should be zero, in that the reproduced signal should be precisely the same as the recorded signal.

Electronic Circuit Requirements

Every tape recorder requires both a record and a reproduce head pre-amplifier, each with its own filtering network. It also requires an ultrasonic oscillator. The oscillator serves two purposes. In the record mode, it provides the AC erase voltage to the erase head. Also, at an attenuated level, it supplies the AC bias voltage to the record head. During reproduction, this oscillator is deactivated, so that no erase or bias voltage is applied.

The oscillator has to comply with two important constraints. Both its output frequency and voltage must be temperature stable and not drift as the equipment warms up. Also, the waveform must be symmetrical. Any asymmetry in its output waveform increases background noise. The oscillator circuit contains an amplified output, so that it can supply sufficient voltage to magnetically saturate the tape as it passes over the erase head. This ensures that the tape is completely erased. In Figure 8-3, it can be seen that there is a *pad* (resistive network) between the oscillator and the record head. Its function is to reduce the oscillator output to a suitable voltage level to supply bias to the record head. This must be low enough that even maximum signal voltage, combined with the bias voltage, does not quite saturate the tape magnetically. Of course, various options are possible. Instead of having separate potentiometers for controlling record and replay gain, a single potentiometer can be used. It is assigned to its appropriate position by operation of the record/replay switch.

The bias trap at the output of the record amplifier prevents any bias voltage from feeding back and overloading the record amplifier output. Similarly, during replay, no ultrasonic bias signal should be amplified by the reproduce amplifier. This explains the positioning of the bias trap.

A more sophisticated professional tape machine might be a modest 4-track portable using ¼-inch tape. Or it might be a 24-track, 1-inch studio recorder designed to operate in conjunction with a console. A typical circuit block diagram for one track of such a machine is shown in Figure 8-4.

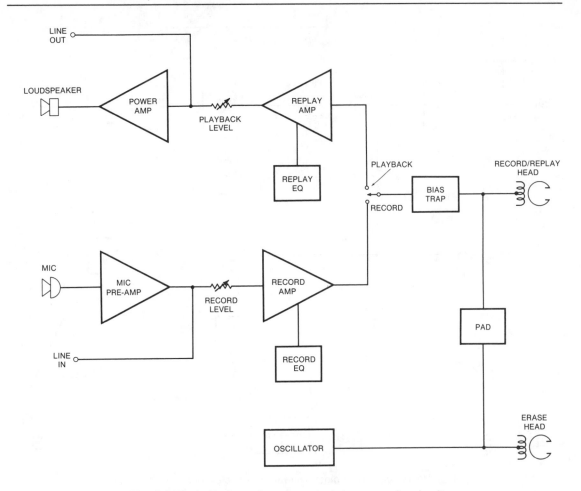

Fig. 8-3 Block diagram of consumer-type tape recorder circuit

The main difference between this and the consumer model is that here there are three heads; a separate head is used for record and reproduce. The advantage of this is that the recording can be monitored directly from the tape by the reproduce head while it is actually being recorded. Also, in this machine, the record and reproduce equalization can be user aligned and the bias can be set by the user to produce optimum results. (See *Tape Recorder Alignment* in Chapter 11.)

Notice that there is no power amplifier or loudspeaker in a studio recorder. The output at line level is intended to be fed to a console or mixer. An independent power amplifier and monitor speakers are installed separately from the recording machine. (However, a professional portable for location recording would probably contain a power amplifier and monitoring speaker.)

Between the bias adjust and record head is a *buffer*. This is an amplifier with a voltage gain of less than unity. It has the effect of reducing the erase voltage to the level needed for biasing the record head. An amplifier is used in this circuit,

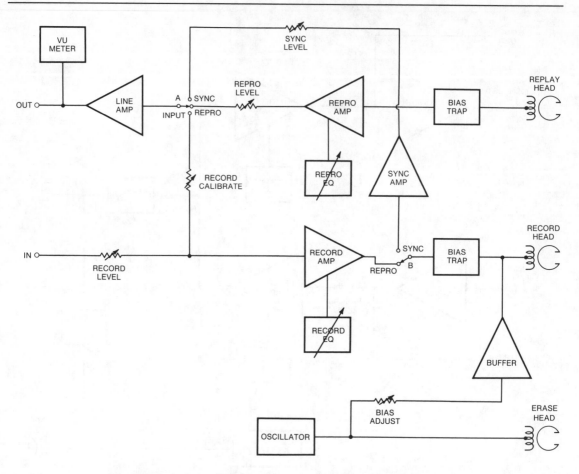

Fig. 8-4 Typical circuit block diagram of a professional tape machine

rather than the passive resistors shown in Figure 8-3, because in this circuit, the bias voltage is adjustable. Such adjustments would cause a change in the current drawn from the oscillator, if a pad were used. This, in turn, would reduce the oscillator stability. By using a buffer instead of a pad, any alteration of power needed to supply bias to the record head is provided by the buffer amplifier, while its input impedance remains unchanged. In this way, the input is buffered from any variation in load at the output. This ensures improved stability in the oscillator's output voltage to the erase head.

You can see from the switch labeled *A* in the repro path of Figure 8-4 that there are three switch positions available. In the Repro position, the tape is reproduced, as would occur during playback or during monitoring of a recording. During a recording (or while setting up prior to a recording session), it is useful to be able to compare the incoming signal with the signal actually being recorded onto the tape. This comparison can be made by switching from Repro to Input and back to Repro again. This does not affect the continuity of the recording. In the Input position, monitoring of the input signal can be obtained before it reaches the recording amplifier. Other than the half-second or so time interval (by which the reproduced signal lags the input, due to the head positioning), there should be no difference in tone or quality between the input and reproduced signal.

Yet another useful facility is the ability to synchronize the recording of one track with a previously made recording on another track. This is useful for overdubbing additional music lines or instruments onto a previous recording. In this way, a single musician can accompany him/herself on a number of different instruments, all to be reproduced simultaneously. For this purpose, the track being reproduced requires that switches *A* and *B* be in the Sync position. You can see from Figure 8-4 that the record head then reproduces the recording from that track, through the sync amplifier to the output. It only remains to patch this output to the monitoring headphones worn by the musician(s), and they can then record onto another track whatever additional music (or speech, or sound effects) are required, while listening to the previous recording.

If the reproduce head were used for synchronizing, any newly recorded signal would be misplaced on the tape by the distance separating the record head from the reproduce head. It would then be about a half-second late. By reproducing from the record head (which is vertically aligned with all other record heads), any new recording exactly synchronizes with the original track. On a multitrack machine, a number of tracks can be mixed down onto a single track using this synchronizing method; however, it is often preferable to mix down onto a separate recorder.

9   Digital Audio

9 Digital Audio

Digital Systems

A system consists of three parts. They are (a) the input sensors, (b) the central processing unit (CPU), and (c) the output devices. Practically everything can be considered a system. A car is a system, a tree is a system, and a human being is a perfect example of a system. In the case of a human, the senses are the input sensors. These are connected by the sensory nervous network to the brain, which is the central processing unit. As a result of certain inputs from the senses, the brain may decide that some action is needed. In this case, command impulses are sent from the brain through the motor nervous network to the appropriate muscles, which are the output devices. This does not mean that a human being is nothing more than a machine. It signifies that a human is capable of making appropriate reactions to his or her environment.

The difference between an analog and a digital system is that in a digital system, processing is done in digital form, using *digital logic*. Digital logic characteristically recognizes only two values: a one or a zero, sometimes called a *high* or a *low*, or alternatively, *true* or *false*. From the viewpoint of digital logic, an analog value that is increasing in a smooth curve is seen as rising in discrete steps.

This difference can be illustrated by comparing an analog and a digital voltmeter. Irrespective of accuracy, the least significant digit displayed by a digital meter must move up in unit steps. If 7 is being displayed, the next higher value must be 8. However, the pointer of an analog meter, which might also be indicating 7, moves over an infinite number of values as it traverses to 8. These might be so close together that they are not readable. But theoretically, the transition is smooth and continuous, whereas in a digital instrument, the movement is in steps.

Because digital values are limited to 1s and 0s, the binary number system is used to store and process numerical quantities. Just as the decimal system is based on 10 (each more significant column being 10 times the value of the previous column), so the binary system is based on 2. Each more significant binary column is twice the value of the previous column. In fact, the binary column values can be thought of as whole number powers of 2. Binary column values are shown below.

Exponential Designation	2^5	2^4	2^3	2^2	2^1	2^0	.	2^{-1}	2^{-2}	2^{-3}
Column Values	32	16	8	4	2	1	.	$\frac{1}{2}$	$\frac{1}{4}$	$\frac{1}{8}$

The binary system lends itself ideally to digital logic, because it contains only two values, either 0 or 1. The value 2 is written as a 1 in the next higher column. For instance, binary 2 is written 10—a 1 in the 2s column and a 0 in the 1s column. Binary 5 is 101—a 1 in the 4s column, 0 in the 2s column, and a 1 in the 1s column. The subscript 2 is added to a binary number to indicate that it is in base 2 form. Subscript 10 is added to a decimal number. Thus, the value of 10_2 is 2, while the value of 10_{10} is 10.

To convert from binary to decimal, simply add the values of all binary columns in which a 1 is present, as shown in Problem 9-1.

Problem 9-1:   Convert binary 1001_2 to decimal.

   Answer: Add the column values:

$$(1 \times 8) + (0 \times 4) + (0 \times 2) + (1 \times 1) = 8 + 0 + 0 + 1 = 9_{10}$$

Because a digital audio system cannot represent a changing value as a smooth curve, it must sample the analog signal at frequent intervals and represent each sample in the form of a binary number. Consequently, an approximation to the analog curve can be built up in the form of discrete steps, each with its own binary value (see Figure 9-1).

Fig. 9-1 Analog vs. digital representation of a signal

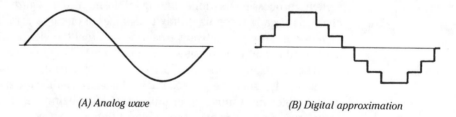

(A) Analog wave   (B) Digital approximation

In the language of digital logic, a group of digits that are combined to form a numerical value (or a single piece of information) is called a *word*. Each piece of data within that word is called a *bit*. The expression "bit" is derived from the two words *binary digit*. The *bi* in *bit* comes from the first two letters of *binary*. The final *t* comes from the final letter in *digit*. So a bit is one piece of digital data, either a high or a low (a 1 or a 0).

A waveform can be more accurately approximated by a large number of small steps, rather than by a few large ones. For instance, a 2-bit word can produce only four binary values: 00, 01, 10, 11. These correspond to 0, 1, 2, 3 in decimal. If a 2-bit quantization system were used, the step size would have to be large and an analog wave would have to be broken down into three increments. If a 3-bit word could be used, eight different values would be possible: namely, 000, 001, 010, 011, 100, 101, 110, 111, corresponding to decimal 0, 1, 2, 3, 4, 5, 6, 7. In this case, the wave could be broken down into seven smaller increments. The greater the number of increments, the more accurate the representation of the wave. This is illustrated in Figure 9-2.

Fig. 9-2
Representation of a wave

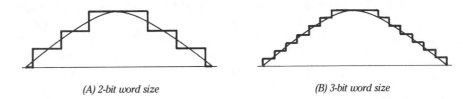

(A) 2-bit word size   (B) 3-bit word size

In fact, the number of possible values for a given word can be calculated from 2^n, where *n* is the number of bits. Thus, the 3-bit word we have used gives 2^3 different values. This is 8, the values being 0 through 7. Although there is an advantage in using large binary words to represent a smooth waveform accurately, there are also disadvantages. The chief disadvantage is the amount of hardware and the cost of large-word processing. A balance has to be reached, and 16 bits is now almost universally accepted as the standard word size for digital audio processing. Many computers are built to handle 16-bit words, and interaction between computers and digital audio is an already developing trend. It is interesting to note the large number of different values that can be obtained using a 16-bit word. The number of values is given by 2^{16}, which is 65,536.

In general then, a digital audio system has to convert an analog waveform into a continuous stream of 16-bit binary numbers. This is called quantization. These numbers can then be digitally processed, equalized, and mixed, have digitally delayed echo added, and be possibly stored in digital form. During reproduction, the signal must again be returned to analog form. So, between the digital processing stage and the power amplifier, conversion is again required— this time from a sequence of binary numbers back to a corresponding analog waveform that represents the air pressure fluctuations needed to generate the final sound. A complete sequence of steps is illustrated in Figure 9-3.

Analog/Digital Interfacing

The analog signal is in the form of a fluctuating voltage. In order to be suitable for digital processing, this signal has to be converted to a series of binary numbers,

Fig. 9-3 Block
diagram of digital
audio chain

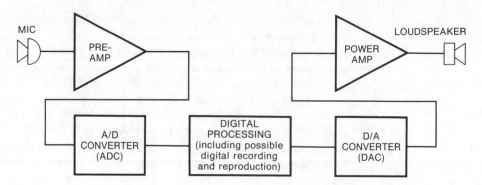

whose values are proportional to the instantaneous voltages of the wave at each
sample moment. The analog-to-digital converter is dedicated to performing this
function. A symbolic representation of this conversion is shown in Figure 9-4. It
uses 4 binary digits, although in reality, 16 binary digits would be used to
quantify each sample.

Fig. 9-4 Analog
waveform
sampling

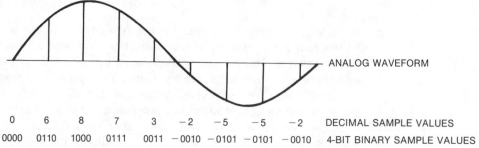

Sampling Requirements

Certain constraints are needed in order to complete the sampling successfully.
Sample times must be precisely spaced, and the sampling frequency must be high
enough so that the highest audible frequency can be adequately represented. A
good quality audio system must reproduce frequencies up to 20 kHz. Because at
least two samples are needed to represent each wave (one in the positive half-
cycle and one in the negative half-cycle), the sampling frequency must be at least
twice the highest audio frequency. Therefore, sampling has to be at or above 40
kHz. In fact, the standard sampling frequency for professional digital magnetic
recording is 48 kHz; for compact disc recording it is 44.1 kHz.

Accurate timing of this sampling process is important. It is controlled by an
electronic *clock*, which produces a square wave at accurate intervals. To achieve
sampling at 48 kHz, for instance, a clock consisting of a square wave generator is
used to produce a 48 kHz waveform. The sampling system can be triggered by the
leading edge of this square wave. Other parts of the digital system need to work
considerably faster, so that processing of each sample can take place in the

interval between samples. Usually the faster clocks oscillate at whole number multiples of the sampling frequency. Frequencies up to a hundred times this clock frequency may be used.

Not only must the voltage from the fluctuating audio signal be extracted precisely at sampling time, but this must be held steady while its value is being converted. The problem is that any electronic component takes a little time to respond to an input signal. This is called the component's *acquisition time*. So the sample value has to be held steady during this period. To achieve this, a *sample and hold* circuit is used. This uses a capacitor and two semiconductor switches that charge the capacitor up to sample voltage at precisely the right moment, where it is held during the required time.

The basic sample and hold circuit is illustrated in Figure 9-5. The two field effect transistors, J_1 and J_2, act as electronic switches. There is a negative voltage at S_1 and S_2 that normally keeps them switched off. The two op-amps B_1 and B_2 are called *buffers*. They output the same voltage as they receive at their inputs, so there is no voltage gain. They can, however, produce high current gain. This prevents current from being drawn from the circuit connected to their inputs. In effect, they buffer this circuit from current drain—hence their name, buffers.

Fig. 9-5 Sample and hold circuit

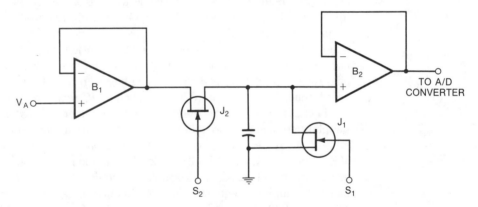

The action of the sample and hold circuit is as follows. Just before sample time, a positive voltage pulse is applied by the clock system at S_1. This momentarily switches on J_1 and discharges the capacitor to ground, so that the previous value is cleared. Then, precisely at sample moment, a positive voltage pulse is applied to S_2, momentarily switching on J_2. This allows a surge of current from op-amp B_1 to charge the top plate of the capacitor to the instantaneous voltage of the analog waveform, V_A. This value is held by the capacitor while the conversion to the corresponding binary value takes place in the A/D converter. Op-amp B_2 allows the required current to be drawn by the A/D converter without discharging the capacitor, so that its voltage remains constant. From this brief description of the sample and hold circuit, it can be seen that conventional electronic components are often used within the framework of a digital system.

Secondary Sampling Requirements

Having examined the main activity of sampling, we have covered the fundamental principles underlying digital audio. However, we must still deal with all sorts of secondary problems that arise. A major problem resulting from sampling is the generation of an audible alias frequency. The word "alias" means a false name. Similarly, an *alias frequency* is a false frequency. It is not true and should not be present. Unfortunately, an alias frequency can be created by the process of sampling. The sampling frequency and the audio signal frequency inevitably come into and out of phase alternately. This produces a third frequency called a *beat*, whose frequency is numerically equal to the difference between the two interacting frequencies.

An example of this occurs in the cinema, when you see the spoked wheel of a car apparently rotating backward, standing still, or rotating slowly forward. This is sometimes called a stroboscopic effect. It is produced by the interaction between the frequency with which a wheel spoke passes a point, and the sampling frequency of the camera. (A movie camera normally takes 24 frames/second.) In this case, a given position of a spoke is in phase with the camera picture at one moment. But, if the camera speed is slightly greater than the spoke frequency (the frequency at which spokes pass a given point), the next picture occurs when the following spoke has not quite reached this position. This difference in phase continues giving the illusion that the wheel is rotating backward. The number of times per second that the spokes come into and out of phase with the camera is the difference between their frequencies. This is why a beat frequency of this nature is also called a *difference* frequency.

Because, in an audio system, the audio frequency is always less than half the sampling frequency, the difference between them must be greater than the highest audio frequency, so it will be ultrasonic and not heard. (For instance, 40K – 15K = 25K, which is ultrasonic.) This would be fine, but there's a snag. Most music instruments produce ultrasonic harmonics. These, being much higher than half the sampling frequency, produce audible alias tones. For instance, a high harmonic of 30 kHz subtracted from a sampling frequency of 40 kHz produces an alias frequency of 10 kHz, which is within the audible range. Here lies the problem; but it can be solved.

Only the high harmonics above 20 kHz (ultrasonic) can cause audible alias frequencies. Therefore, a low-pass filter is installed just before the sampling stage. This is designed to cut off sharply all high harmonics above 20 kHz, while leaving the audible range of frequencies intact. By eliminating these high harmonics, the resulting alias frequencies are also eliminated. This low-pass filter is called an *anti-alias* filter.

One other worrisome little situation exists. Both during quiet passages and during pauses, background noise in a digital audio system is different from *white noise*. White noise is the natural noise in our surroundings. It consists of equal levels of all frequencies combined in a random manner. It is also the type of noise produced by an analog system, so it can be accepted by the listener.

In digital audio, the stepped nature of low-level sound, such as background noise, is not "white." It sounds like low-level clicking and is called *granulation noise*. This is not acceptable; in fact, it is quite objectionable to the ear. Adding a low-level audio signal made up of white noise just before the anti-alias filter adds a random element that eliminates this problem. This added white noise is called *dither*. Its amplitude needs to be only about one-third step size, so it barely increases the noise level. A dither generator, therefore, eliminates this granulation noise problem entirely.

Let us now summarize the process involved in digital audio systems, as it has been described up to now. The fundamental requirement is the sampling of the analog waveform at just over 40,000 times/second. At each sampling moment, the instantaneous voltage of the wave is measured and converted to a binary numerical value. This conversion process is performed by the analog-to-digital converter (ADC), which acts as a digital voltmeter whose readout is binary. A number of secondary processes are needed to ensure that the sampling process is completed successfully. These are

1. Addition of low-level white noise called dither. This is needed to convert background noise from unacceptable granulation to white noise.
2. Filtering of the analog signal by an anti-alias filter. This prevents generation of audible alias frequencies.
3. Use of a sample and hold circuit prior to A/D conversion. This ensures accurate quantization at precise sampling moments.

D/A and A/D Conversion

After digital processing (and during reproduction of a digital recording), the sampling process has to be reversed, to convert the sampled binary values back to a sequence of voltages. This automatically reconstructs the analog waveform, which is then amplified by the power amplifier and fed to loudspeakers. A block diagram of the overall sequence is illustrated earlier in Figure 9-3. Just as secondary problems associated with sampling must be overcome during A/D conversion, there are also two secondary problems during D/A conversion. The first requires the use of an output sample and hold circuit. The second requires another low-pass filter just before the power amplifier. This output LP filter also has a cutoff frequency of 20 kHz, but it is called an *anti-imaging* filter. The precise need for and function of these two secondary components will be described shortly. First it is necessary to say something about the two main components in the digitization process: the A/D converter and the D/A converter. Their positions in the audio chain are shown earlier in Figure 9-3.

Both A/D and D/A converters perform the fundamental requirements of the digital processing and recording of an audio signal. The A/D converter converts an instantaneous voltage to a binary value. The D/A converter converts a binary value to an instantaneous voltage. Although the A/D converter occurs first in the audio chain, I will describe the D/A converter first, because a D/A converter is included in the architecture of the A/D converter. Therefore, it is necessary to have some idea of how it works before dealing with the more complex circuit.

The function of the D/A converter is to convert a binary value to a corresponding voltage, which is proportional to the value. There are several ways to do this. Perhaps the simplest method uses a summing op-amp (described in some detail in Chapter 3).

Instead of summing all of the input channels equally, however, we must give each input a voltage gain that corresponds to its column position in the binary number system. The circuit of a summing amplifier is illustrated in Chapter 3 (Figure 3-7). The expression for its output voltage is

$$V_o = V_1 \frac{R_f}{R_1} + V_2 \frac{R_f}{R_2} + V_3 \frac{R_f}{R_3} + \ldots$$

This formula can be thought of as summing each input voltage times its channel gain. To convert a binary number to a corresponding voltage, all that is needed is to amplify each more significant column with twice the gain of the previous column. A simple 5-bit digital-to-analog converter can be made in this way (see Figure 9-6).

Fig. 9-6 5-bit digital-to-analog converter

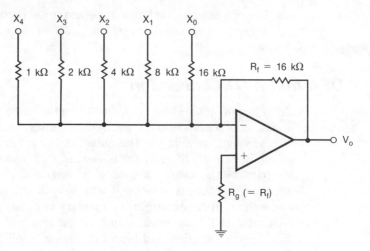

If the inputs consist of a 5-bit binary number, which we will call X, then its digits are X_4, X_3, X_2, X_1, X_0. R_f is the multiplier. By varying R_f, the maximum output voltage can be adjusted to any required value, while the proportionality of the inputs remains unchanged. (In a digital system, 16 input bits are needed, but conversion is achieved in the same way.)

Consider a binary input of 11001. For the sake of this example, we will consider a logic high to be 1 V. Of course, a logic low is 0 V. Then the output voltage is given by

$$V_o = \left(1 \times \frac{16K}{1K}\right) + \left(1 \times \frac{16K}{2K}\right) + \left(0 \times \frac{16K}{4K}\right) + \left(0 \times \frac{16K}{8K}\right) + \left(1 \times \frac{16K}{16K}\right)$$

$$= 16 + 8 + 0 + 0 + 1$$

$$= 25\ V$$

The decimal value of 11001_2 is 25. So it is clear that the output voltage of this converter exactly corresponds to the value of the binary input. However, there is a small problem associated with this conversion process. At the moment of transition from one voltage to the next, there is a short *glitch*. This is a sudden, false, fluctuating output voltage that occurs just before the new output voltage has stabilized. These glitches have to be eliminated or the output waveform might look something like that in Figure 9-7.

Fig. 9-7
Uncorrected
output glitches

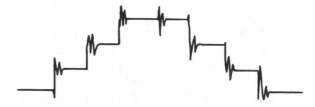

To solve this problem, the output sample and hold circuit is installed just after the D/A converter. This samples the true value of each step *after* the fluctuations have ceased, and holds that value until the next sampling moment. That is *after* the next output value has stabilized.

We are now left with a waveform that corresponds to the required analog output except that it is made up of numerous, small voltage steps. By passing this stepped waveform through a low-pass filter, called the anti-imaging filter, the vertical transients (the leading and trailing edges of the square wave) can be shaped sufficiently, so that a perfectly smooth analog waveform is obtained.

The cutoff point of this final output filter is 20 kHz, so it passes all audio frequencies and still effectively smoothes out the steps into a continuous curve. It is interesting to note that the entire digital process starts and ends with low-pass filters that have a cutoff frequency of 20 kHz. These are the anti-alias filter and the anti-imaging filter, respectively.

Now we can describe how the A/D converter works. Its purpose is to convert the instantaneous sample voltage to a binary value. The method most often used in digital audio systems is called the *successive approximation register* (SAR), a block diagram of which is shown in Figure 9-8.

Each bit in the 16-bit register, from the most significant to the least, is rapidly tested by the converter's control unit, first with a 1, then with a 0, until the binary value is found that most closely corresponds to the analog voltage.

The control unit contains, in addition to other circuitry, a slow and a fast clock. The slow clock speed is that of sampling frequency. At each sampling moment, it clears the 16-bit register by resetting it to 0. Then the fast clock

Fig. 9-8
Successive
approximation
register (A/D
converter)

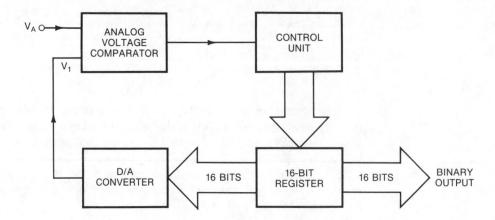

sequentially tests each bit in the register, starting at the most significant bit (on the left) with a 1; then, if the binary value is too high, changing it to a 0. Meanwhile, the binary value is fed to the D/A converter, where it is converted to a corresponding analog voltage, V_1, which is compared by the analog voltage comparator with the input voltage, V_A. If it is too high, the comparator outputs a high, telling the control unit to change that bit to a 0. If it is too low, the comparator output goes low, telling the control unit to keep it as 1. In this way, the A/D converter rapidly converts an instantaneous voltage to its binary value, where it is held until the next sampling moment. The cycle is then repeated. A block diagram of the stages before and after the central processing unit is shown in Figure 9-9.

Digital Audio Applications

Digital audio data can be recorded onto any digital storage medium. Each different medium requires its own processing and modulation method, both for recording and reproduction. As a result, considerably more than 16 bits of binary data per sample have to be made available for successful storage (of course, stereo recording doubles the audio data). Additional data containing processing information is also needed. These additional data bits are called *redundant* bits.

Part of this redundant data consists of a synchronizing code that identifies the start of each binary word. Another part contains an error detection and correction code, which enables a comparison to be made of reproduced and recorded data. This error detection system allows the reproduction processing stage to determine if an error has occurred. In addition, it usually permits the error to be corrected. If this is not possible, an automatic error concealment system is activated, so that the error is not noticed.

Stereo audio samples require 32 bits of data (two 16-bit channels) to be recorded at a rate of just over 40 kHz. This requires a recording frequency of

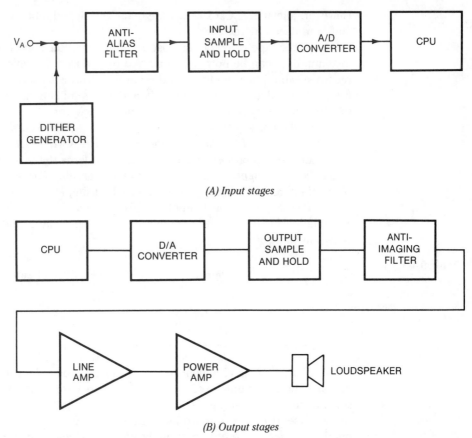

(A) Input stages

(B) Output stages

Fig. 9-9 Block diagram of digital audio system

about $1\frac{1}{4}$ million bits/second. The additional redundant data that also has to be included brings the total digital data to be recorded up to about $4\frac{1}{4}$ million bits/second. This high-frequency requirement presents limitations and challenges peculiar to digital audio recording. Because of this, the average computer memory is able only to hold comparatively short sequences of music. The most useful memory storage medium for digital audio is magnetic tape or compact disc.

A compact disc can store an hour of digitally recorded music. Its reproduction quality is superior to an LP disc in frequency range, reduced background noise and consequent increased dynamic range, reduced harmonic distortion, longevity (being sensed by a laser rather than a stylus), improved wow and flutter characteristics, and in general, a more life-like quality of sound.

The recordings are produced by imprinting microscopic pits onto the flat surface of a substrate. During reproduction, the sensing laser is processed to interpret a pit edge (an upward or downward transition at the start or end of a pit) as a logic high. A flat surface is interpreted as a logic low. Currently, most compact discs are recorded by the manufacturer and can be used only for reproduction.

However, alternative CD formats are being developed that can be both recorded and reproduced by the user.

Magnetic tape is the other most useful medium for digital recording. On this medium, data can be both recorded and reproduced; however, an analog audio recorder cannot be used for digital recording. This is because the high recording frequency needed to accept digital data at over 4 million bits/second is far above the top frequency threshold of an analog recorder. There are two types of specialized recorders that can be used to magnetically record digital audio.

One is the *digital audio stationary head* (DASH) recording machine. This really consists of a professional multitrack recorder with the necessary processing stage added to adapt the digital data to the recording format. This machine can successfully record very high frequencies by using a high tape speed. Or it can synchronously record on multiple heads to compensate for lower tape speeds. The relationship between the number of heads per channel and the tape speed is shown in Table 9-1.

Table 9-1
Relationship between tape speed and heads per channel

Tape Speed	Heads Per Channel
$7\frac{1}{2}$ ips	4
15 ips	2
30 ips	1

At 30 ips, the high frequencies can be achieved by a single head. At 15 ips, the digital data is demultiplexed (divided into two parallel streams) and recorded simultaneously on two heads. Each head records half of the data. On playback, these same two heads reproduce the two recorded tracks, which are then multiplexed (combined) onto a single line, to achieve the original sequence of digital data. Similarly, at half this speed, four heads are used synchronously, each head recording a quarter of the data onto four separate tracks.

The other type of magnetic recorder that can be used comes under the category of *rotary head* machines. In fact, it is a video recorder with a specialized digital processing stage that adapts the digital data to a format suitable for recording on a video recorder. Video machines are designed for very-high-frequency recording, so there is no problem with frequency limitations. The recording heads rotate at high speed inside a helical tape guide drum, so that the heads write thin, diagonal tracks onto the slowly moving tape as it passes.

Both professional and consumer recorders of this type are available. Most CDs are mastered in this way from a rotary head recording machine. From the consumer's viewpoint, digital recording equipment—even the video recorder combined with the necessary processing stages—is costly. However, a new recording format has recently been introduced. This is known as R-DAT, which stands for *rotary digital audio tape*, or simply DAT. Its development is already bringing digital audio recording within the reach of audio enthusiasts as well as serious musicians.

Advantages of Digital Audio

It has been mentioned that compact disc specifications are superior to LP discs in many respects, most notably in lower background noise and increased dynamic range. Background noise is quite different in digital systems than in analog systems.

In the analog system, it is largely the current flow through transistors (or tubes), amplified in stage after stage, that causes background noise. There is also added tape hiss in tape recording. One result is that each time an analog recording is re-recorded, the background noise and any equalization errors are increased. This tends to cause degradation of quality after a number of re-recordings.

In digital systems, noise is of a different nature. It is not noise, as such, but quantization errors that cause the problem. Although an analog waveform is broken down into an extremely large number of very small steps, there is still some error probability in each step. This, of course, becomes more noticeable in quiet passages, when the step size becomes large compared to the wave amplitude. The maximum possible quantization error amounts to half the step size (see Figure 9-10).

Fig. 9-10
Maximum
quantization error

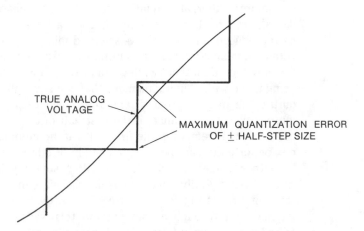

The ratio of signal to noise in an analog system is given by the maximum signal voltage divided by the noise voltage. In a digital system, this ratio is strictly speaking a signal-to-error ratio. This is a value equal to the maximum number of steps (corresponding to maximum signal) divided by the maximum error, which is half a step. As noted earlier, to overcome the problem of granulation noise, white noise in the form of dither at one-third step size is added to the signal. This converts the signal-to-error ratio into what can justifiably now be called signal-to-noise ratio, the granulation noise having been converted to white noise.

In a 16-bit system, the digital signal-to-noise level is about 98 dB, taking into account quantization errors and added dither. In fact, most digital components are specified as having a signal-to-noise level of "over 90 dB." This compares favorably with analog tape recorders, in which the figure is about 65 dB.

Digital systems have another advantage over analog, in that when re-recording, the noise level does not increase. Consequently, digital recordings can be re-recorded many times. The reason for this is that the quantization error occurs only during sampling. Provided the digital signal is reproduced and re-recorded in digital form, sampling does not have to occur again; therefore, there is no increase in noise. Tape hiss and transistor noise have no effect, because they are always at such a low voltage that they are interpreted as a logic 0. From the point of view of subsequent logical analysis, they don't exist.

Another important advantage of digital audio lies in the field of signal processing. The processing that has been described so far has been a necessary part of analog/digital interfacing in digital recording and reproduction. Once the analog signal has been successfully converted to digital and fed to the central processing unit, any amount of additional processing can be applied. All of the acceptable state-of-the-art processes that a modern analog console can achieve can also be achieved digitally. For instance, a digital console can digitally mix numerous input channels; it can apply digital delay and reverb; and it can expand or compress, filter, and equalize any or all of the channels. Then, of course, it can digitally record these onto a multitrack master. At a later time, these tracks can be reproduced through the console and mixed down to a stereo master, just as with an analog console and multitrack recording system.

However, digital processing can also do more. Many digital consoles are now being made with a digital memory that can remember all of the operations made during the mixing process, and reproduce these operations without human intervention. For instance, if the first half of a mixdown is perfect, but a short passage needs remixing, the first half can be automatically repeated and a new mix opportunity can then be punched in or edited as needed.

Other, sometimes strange and often superbly imaginative, effects can be created on digitally recorded sounds. This can be achieved by writing the relevant processing in the form of a software program instruction set and interfacing it through a computer. In this way, audio processing is becoming available to an extent far beyond what was previously available to the analog audio engineer. It can fairly be said that what can be done by interfacing computers with digital audio extends future processing possibilities to the limits of human imagination. This newly developing situation offers great problems, great challenges, and vast possibilities for the future of one of the most important of human activities—making music.

10 Practical Audio Circuits

10 Practical Audio Circuits

Power Supplies

All active electronic circuits need to be energized by a DC source of suitable voltage. For most applications, it is convenient or absolutely necessary to use the AC line voltage as an energy source. In these cases, the AC line leads directly to the *power supply* inside the component cabinet. It is the function of this power supply to convert the 115 V AC current to a DC source of suitable voltage to drive the electronic circuits. Sometimes a number of different voltages are needed. The power supply can be adapted to supply these.

It is useful and necessary to know how a power supply works, because all line-powered circuits contain one, and it is the first stage to be tested when troubleshooting or repairing a faulty component.

There are three main parts to a power supply. They are

1. *The transformer*. This transforms the 115 V line voltage to just above the final required voltage. For transistor circuits, this can be anything from 5 V to 35 V. For vacuum tube circuits, this can be in the region of 250 V or more.

2. *The rectifier*. This converts the AC voltage from the transformer secondary to a DC voltage. However, it is a pulsating DC, not a smooth DC, and a smooth DC is needed to energize the electronic circuits.

3. *The smoothing and regulating stage*. Here the pulsating DC is changed to a smooth DC, largely by use of a smoothing capacitor. Due to internal resistances of the secondary coil and rectifiers, the output voltage of this smoothed DC is not entirely stable. When current is drawn, the voltage falls

in proportion to the amount of current. So this stage usually includes a regulating device that maintains virtually constant output voltage, however much current is drawn (within the limits for which the power supply was designed to operate).

Let us now examine each stage in detail. In the next section, we will see how to construct a power supply that is useful for powering commonly used signal processing components.

The Transformer

A transformer consists of a primary and a secondary coil. The more powerful the transformer, the larger and more costly it is, because it requires more iron in its core and larger coils. Don't overload a transformer or it will overheat and it might burn out.

The secondary consists of a coil with or without taps; it can also consist of several coils, depending on how many different output voltages are needed, and also on the type of rectifier that is used.

The Rectifier

Rectification is the process of converting an AC source to DC. There are two main types of rectifier. One is the half-wave rectifier, which uses only one diode. The other is the full-wave rectifier. This latter can be divided into two categories: the full-wave rectifier that uses two diodes, and the bridge rectifier that uses four diodes. Figure 10-1 illustrates the transformer with the secondary connected to the different types of rectifier.

The diode is the active component in all of these rectifiers. Notice that the terminals of the transformer secondary oscillate in reverse polarity to each other. When the top terminal is positive, the bottom terminal is negative. In the next half-cycle, both polarities reverse, so you can trace the current flow during each half-cycle.

Look first at Figure 10-1A. In the first half-cycle, point X is positive and point Y is negative, so electron flow is from Y, up through the load resistor, through the diode (with no opposition, because diodes conduct electrons in the opposite direction to the arrow), and back to X, the most positive point in the circuit. The electromagnetic action then forces the current down through the secondary and out again at point Y. This is the complete circuit during the first half-cycle. Note that electron flow is upward through the load; therefore, the top terminal of the load must be positive (electrons flow only to a more positive voltage).

In the second half-cycle, electrons try to flow out of point X, which is now negative. They are attracted to point Y; however, they cannot pass through the diode in the direction of its arrow, because the diode is now reverse biased. Therefore, no current flows in the circuit in the second half-cycle. All of the voltage develops across the diode, none across the load, and no current flows through the load. Because current flows only during one-half of the cycle, this is called a half-wave rectifier, and the output consists of fluctuating positive half-cycles only. This is illustrated in the waveform drawn in the top right corner of the diagram in Figure 10-1A. Because there are half-wave gaps between each DC pulse, a large, comparatively costly smoothing capacitor is needed to smooth out these pulsations. But in all other respects, it is a simple and effective circuit.

We can now examine the two-diode full-wave rectifier in Figure 10-1B. Notice that this requires a center tapped secondary. The center tap is held at ground potential.

In the first half-cycle, the current flow is shown by the heavier dashed line. It is true that current (electron flow) tends to originate from the most negative point, namely Y, but it can't pass the diode in its reverse biased polarity, so no current flows through the bottom half of the coil. However, current can flow from the center tap (which is at ground potential), up through the load, and back through the top diode to point X, the positive terminal. Therefore, only the top diode and top half of the secondary conducts during the first half-cycle.

In the second half-cycle, all polarities are reversed, and the current flow is shown by the lighter dashed line. Again, current can leave the secondary only by the center tap. It flows again upward through the load and back through the bottom diode (which is now forward biased) to point Y. Thus, only the bottom half of the coil conducts during the second half-cycle. This type of rectifier has the disadvantage of requiring a double length of secondary coil with a center tap. This adds to the cost of the transformer. You will notice from the waveform shown that a DC voltage occurs during both half-cycles; hence its name, *full-wave rectifier*. The fact that there are no half-wave intervals between pulses means that it is easier to smooth this waveform, so a smaller and less costly smoothing capacitor is adequate. However, this benefit is countered by the need for a more costly center tapped transformer. There is not much choice between the one-diode and two-diode circuits, in cost or effectiveness.

Figure 10-1C illustrates a bridge rectifier. The advantage of this is that the whole transformer secondary is used in both half-cycles, and there is no center tap. This keeps down the transformer cost. Also, the full wave is rectified, which means that the same comparatively small smoothing capacitor can be used as was suitable for the two-diode circuit. For the added cost of two extra diodes (which is negligible), this circuit incorporates the advantages of both previous circuits with none of the disadvantages. The first half-cycle current flow is shown by the lighter dashed line, the second half-cycle by the heavier dashed line. Notice that two diodes conduct in the first half-cycle. The other two conduct during the second half-cycle. The discriminating factor is the direction of bias that is applied to the diodes.

In the first half-cycle, electron flow is from point Y. At the bottom of the bridge, only D_1 can conduct. (Electrons cannot flow in the same direction as the arrow.) From the DC negative point, current cannot pass D_2, so it goes through the ground bus, up through the load to the DC positive, and then through D_3. Therefore, only D_1 and D_3 conduct in the first half-cycle, and D_2 and D_4 conduct in the second half-cycle.

Fig. 10-1
Transformer and
rectifier stages

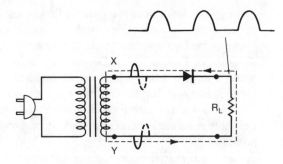

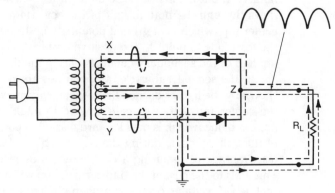

(A) Transformer feeding a half-wave rectifier

(B) Transformer feeding a two-diode full-wave rectifier

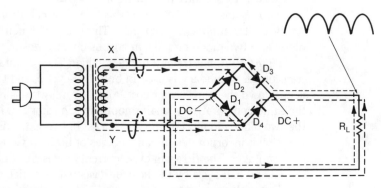

(C) Transformer feeding a bridge rectifier

The Smoothing and Regulating Stage

In Figure 10-1, the rectifier is shown connected directly to the load. This is done so that the current paths through the rectifier can be clearly seen. But in fact, there is always a smoothing and regulating stage between the rectifier and the load.

A capacitor is a device for storing electrical energy in the form of a charge. It is this ability to store electrical energy that enables it to smooth out most of the pulsations and fluctuations that emerge from the rectifier stage (see Figure 10-2B). In fact, it is usually possible to locate the power supply in any electronic circuit simply by looking for the largest electrolytic capacitor.

Fig. 10-2
Smoothing
capacitor action
in a power supply

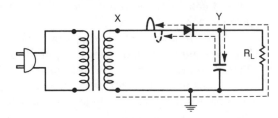

(A) Smoothing capacitor following half-wave rectifier

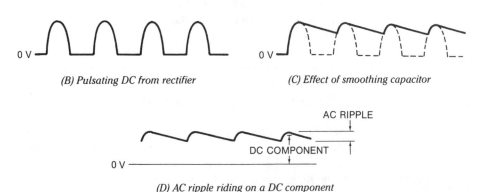

(B) Pulsating DC from rectifier | *(C) Effect of smoothing capacitor*

(D) AC ripple riding on a DC component

The capacitor acts as an electronic shock absorber. It absorbs energy in the form of a charge when the rectified voltage is at its peaks, and it gives back energy when the voltage falls to its troughs. This is the basic smoothing action. Let us look at the simple half-wave rectified power supply circuit in Figure 10-2A, to obtain a clearer picture of the smoothing capacitor's action. Assume that the bottom terminal of the secondary is grounded and that all AC voltage fluctuates at the top secondary terminal. We need only consider the first half-cycle, because no current can flow in the second half-cycle, due to the action of the diode.

When the power supply is first switched on, the rectified voltage rises to its first peak and charges the top plate of the capacitor to peak value. From the schematic in Figure 10-2A, you can see that current (electron flow) passes not only through the load to point X (the peak positive polarity), but also from the top plate of the capacitor to point X. It is this flow of electrons from the capacitor's top plate that causes it to become charged to the positive peak. (Absence of negatively charged electrons is what causes the plate to become positively charged.)

Shortly, the rectified voltage falls to zero (see Figure 10-2B). This is where the capacitor's value comes in. The top plate of the capacitor still remains at positive peak voltage. The result is that current can continue to flow upward through the load. When this current reaches point Y, it turns downward onto the top plate of the capacitor, which is now the most positive point in the circuit. In this way, current can continue to flow through the load, although the rectifier output has fallen to zero.

As current (electrons) accumulates on the capacitor's top plate, it gradually becomes more and more negative; in other words, it loses some of its positive charge and so its voltage drops. But it is such a large capacitor that its voltage hasn't time to fall very far before the next positive peak from the rectifier occurs and charges the capacitor up to its peak voltage again. The resulting output from this rectifying and smoothing stage is shown in Figure 10-2C. After the initial surge, caused when the power is first switched on, the voltage settles down to a rippling effect averaging just below peak value. This waveform can be described as an AC ripple riding on the shoulders of a DC component, as shown in Figure 10-2D. (AC ripple results in hum.) For good quality power supply action, the AC ripple should be very small compared with the DC component. In fact, the ripple from the smoothing capacitor can be almost completely eliminated by the regulator that follows.

Without a regulator, the output voltage of the power supply would be affected by the current flow. A small current flow would not discharge the smoothing capacitor much, nor would it produce much drop in the resistances of the diodes and secondary. But at maximum current flow, the resistances and capacitor discharge level would cause a loss of about 20 percent of the output voltage. Such voltage fluctuations would cause serious problems in electronic circuits. What the regulator does is to reduce the voltage to about 70 percent of its maximum value at all times. This is just below the level to which it would fall under maximum current conditions. In this way, the output voltage remains substantially constant, whatever current might be drawn.

The voltage regulator consists of a constant voltage circuit made up of one or more transistors; but these days, nobody bothers to construct his own voltage regulator. These are mass produced for the electronics industry in the form of a chip, or inexpensive circuit. A person simply purchases either a positive or negative regulator designed to output whatever voltage is required. Usually, for transistorized circuits, a 12 V or 15 V regulator is used. Thus, the final power supply circuit might be like that shown in Figure 10-3A. This is a bridge rectified positive output power supply.

An advantage of the regulator is that it serves two important purposes. By using a suitable value of about 70 percent of the peak secondary voltage, it not only regulates the output voltage, keeping it constant at all normal loads, it also cuts out the AC ripple that results from the effect of the smoothing capacitor. The smoothing capacitor is chosen to be of sufficient capacitance so that the voltage never falls below 70 percent of peak value, even when maximum current is drawn. Because the RMS (Root Mean Square) value of an AC voltage is just over 70

Fig. 10-3 Bridge rectified positive output power supply

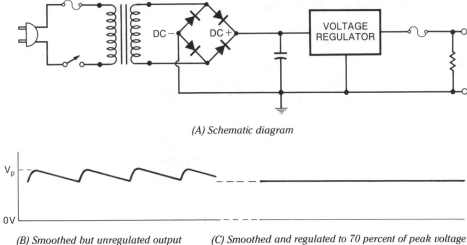

(A) Schematic diagram

(B) Smoothed but unregulated output   *(C) Smoothed and regulated to 70 percent of peak voltage*

percent of its peak value, it works out that the rated secondary voltage of the transformer should be just over the required output value of the voltage regulator—about 15 percent over to allow for losses due to resistance in the rectifier stage. For a regulated output of 12 V, a transformer secondary voltage of about 12.6 V to 15 V is suitable. For an output of 15 V, a secondary of about 16 V to 18 V is suitable.

Power Supply Construction

The power supply circuit described here corresponds to that illustrated in Figure 10-3A. The theory of its action has already been covered in detail. The first step in construction consists of deciding on a suitable layout for the components. A suggested layout is shown in Figure 10-4.

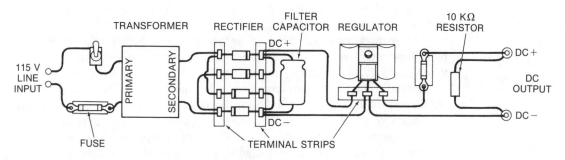

Fig. 10-4 Suggested layout for power supply

List of Components

1	Cabinet
1	Transformer (Primary 115 V, Secondary 12.6 V to 16 V, 250 mA approximately)
4	Silicon diode rectifiers (1 A)
1	Electrolytic capacitor (500 μF, 30 V, axial)
1	Voltage regulator (7812)
1	Heat sink to fit voltage regulator
1	Tube, heat sink compound
3	Terminal strips (4 or 5 tag)
3	Assorted colors of hook-up wire (20 gauge, solid)
2	Terminal posts (one red and one black)
1	Line cable with plug
2	Fuse holders
1	Slow-blow fuse ($\frac{1}{2}$ A)
1	Quick-blow fuse (1 A)
1	Resistor ($\frac{1}{2}$ W, 10 kΩ approximately)

Construction Procedure

Notice in Figure 10-4 that the stages have been laid out in sequence from the line input on the left to the DC output on the right. Drill a few equally spaced ventilation holes at the bottom of one end and at the top of the other end. This will allow convection air flow to cool the components. Pass the line cable through its access hole on the left. With plenty of slack inside, tie a knot inside the access hole to anchor the cable. Drill fixing holes for all of the components.

Keep the wiring tidy. Use exact lengths of wire, and make all bends right angles by bending with long nose pliers. The three terminal strips consist of four or five solder tags fixed to an insulated strip. The tag connected to the fixing bracket should be used for a ground connection only. No voltage must be affixed to it, because the fixing bolt extends through the cabinet. For professional results, color code all hook-up wiring: AC should be green or blue, DC+ should be red, and DC− and ground should be black.

The cathode end of a diode is the one indicated by the silver band. When more than one wire has to be connected to any one soldering tag, anchor each wire separately, but do not solder until each has been put into place.

Spread a little heat sink compound on the back plate of the voltage regulator before bolting it to the heat sink, and fix the regulator to the heat sink before soldering into place. This helps to keep the regulator cool during soldering.

Test each stage as it is completed. When the transformer has been installed, insert the line voltage fuse ($\frac{1}{2}$ A slow-blow) and line plug, and test to obtain 115

AC volts at the primary and approximately 16 AC volts at the secondary. Don't forget to remove the line plug before continuing with the construction.

The rectifier output should be approximately 20 DC volts when the smoothing capacitor has been installed. When installing this capacitor, make sure it is polarized correctly. If incorrectly polarized, the capacitor will work for a few seconds, then overheat and blow up.

The unregulated voltage at the regulator input should be the same as across the capacitor—about 20 V. The regulated output voltage should be 12 DC volts. The 10 kΩ resistor across the output terminals is merely to ensure slight current flow to maintain correct regulator voltages.

For a given power, far less current flows at the high-voltage input than at the low-voltage output. For this reason, the ½ A fuse is used for the line voltage and the 1 A fuse for the DC output. When the power is first switched on, a sudden surge of current flows through the rectifier to charge the capacitor; therefore, a slow-blow fuse is assigned to the input. It permits this momentary surge to exceed its rated value for a short period, while still ensuring that not more than ½ A will flow long enough to cause damage. The 1 A output fuse protects the regulator from burnout, should the output be short circuited.

Signal Tracer Construction

A signal tracer consists of a low-power audio amplifier connected to a small loudspeaker. It is useful during troubleshooting because it can audibly detect an audio signal between stages of an amplification chain. A signal tracer schematic is shown in Figure 10-5A. It is similar to the inverting op-amp discussed in Chapter 3, and the amplification theory is the same.

The integrated circuit pin connections are identified in Figure 10-5B. Note that pins 2 and 3 are the inverting and non-inverting signal inputs. They have nothing to do with battery + and −. The battery is connected between pin 6 and ground.

As was mentioned in Chapter 3, the gain of an inverting op-amp is given by R_f/R_i, which in this schematic is R_2/R_1 or 680 kΩ/100 kΩ, which is 6.8. This should be adequate for our purposes.

It is not possible to use a regular op-amp, because it has insufficient power to drive a loudspeaker. The op-amp used in this circuit is the 386. It includes a power amplifier output stage that can produce up to 0.4 W of audio power. This is quite sufficient to drive the small loudspeaker in our signal tracer, with more than enough volume. A power supply consisting of a 9 V battery makes the unit completely portable.

Volume control is provided by the 10 kΩ potentiometer, R_4 in the schematic. This potentiometer configuration is a standard circuit for gain or volume control in almost any audio circuit.

A potentiometer consists of a fixed resistor between the outer terminals (pins 3 and 1), and a moving wiper, which is the center terminal (pin 2) in the

Fig. 10-5 Signal
tracer

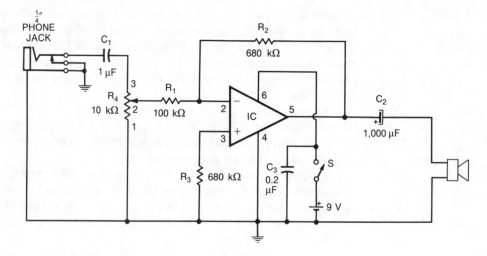

(A) Schematic

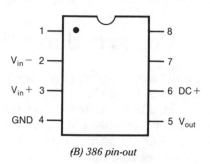

(B) 386 pin-out

schematic. The wiper can move up and down the fixed resistor, as indicated by
the arrow in the schematic symbol. The fixed resistor acts as the load to the
incoming signal. The wiper taps off progressively lower signal voltages as it
moves down from pin 3 (maximum signal) to pin 1, which is connected to ground
where the signal is zero.

In some situations, such as the shelving equalizer described in Chapter 5, a
linear potentiometer is used. Linear taper means that the resistive element is of
constant resistivity throughout its length, so the resistance between points 1 and 2
is linearly proportional to the distance moved by the wiper (slider in a slide
potentiometer, or knob rotation in a rotary potentiometer). However, this type is
not suitable as a volume control.

Because the subjective experience of an increase in loudness is logarithmic, a
large signal increase at high listening levels gives the same apparent loudness
increase as a small signal increase at low listening levels. For this reason, the
resistive element in a volume control is *tapered* in such a way that the resistivity
rises at an ever increasing rate as the wiper is moved up. This type of

potentiometer is said to have a logarithmic or *audio* taper. The loudness appears to increase linearly in proportion to knob rotation.

If a linear potentiometer were used, all of the loudness increase would appear to occur at the start of the knob rotation, and the remaining rotation would appear to do practically nothing. It is important, therefore, not to connect the outer terminals of the potentiometer (pins 3 and 1) in reverse. This would make the apparent lack of linearity worse instead of better.

To ensure that the response of the potentiometer remains logarithmic, it is necessary that the input resistance of the following circuit (R_1 in Figure 10-5A) be high compared to the resistance of the potentiometer. If it were equal to or lower than that of the potentiometer, it would tend to short the lower section of the potentiometer to ground, thus distorting its logarithmic taper. A suitable value for R_1, therefore, is ten times higher than the resistance of the potentiometer; its effect is then negligible. That's why it is specified as 100 kΩ. In consequence, R_2 is necessarily set at 680 kΩ to obtain the required 6.8 gain.

Because a unipolar positive power supply is used (the 9 V battery), the output from pin 5 consists of an AC signal riding on the shoulders of a DC component. A coupling capacitor, C_2, is therefore necessary to block the DC while coupling the AC signal to the loudspeaker. Note that the positive terminal of the capacitor must go to pin 5. C_2 in series with the effective resistance of the loudspeaker forms a high-pass filter. It is necessary to ensure that its cutoff frequency is low enough to pass all audio frequencies without significant loss. Assuming a 4 Ω speaker, the cutoff frequency occurs when the reactance of the capacitor rises to 4 Ω. However, this small speaker cannot, and need not, output very low frequencies, so we can permit cutoff at 40 Hz. The calculations for finding a suitable capacitance for C_2 are, therefore,

$$X_{C2} = \frac{1}{2\pi f C_2}$$

So,

$$C_2 = \frac{1}{2\pi f X_{C2}}$$

Cutoff occurs when $X_{C2} = R$; therefore, substituting R for X_{C2}, we get

$$C_2 = \frac{1}{2\pi f R}$$

With f = 40 Hz and R = 4 Ω,

$$C_2 = \frac{1}{2\pi \times 40 \times 4}$$

So,

$$C_2 = 995 \ \mu F \approx 1000 \ \mu F$$

Thus, we can use a 1,000 μF capacitor. It would be a good idea to have the maximum working voltage of this capacitor high enough to exceed the 9 V battery potential. I have, therefore, specified 12 V as its voltage.

It is also advisable to isolate any DC component that may accompany the signal input, so a coupling capacitor, C_1, is required. This capacitor, in series with the 10 kΩ potentiometer, forms a high-pass filter; therefore, its reactance at the lowest audible frequency should not be more than 10 kΩ. Because of this high input resistance, a much smaller capacitor can be used than was needed to couple the 4 Ω loudspeaker. This input capacitor need be only about 2 μF, with a working voltage of 100 V.

The 0.2 μF capacitor, C_3, is described as a decoupling capacitor. It decouples the signal from the 9 V battery feeding the amplifier between pins 6 and 4. To understand the need for this, remember what was said in Chapter 1 about the generator part of a circuit.

Every voltage source must be assumed to be in series with an output resistance. In this case, it is the internal resistance of the 9 V battery with which we are concerned. As the amplifier's current drain from the battery fluctuates, increasing at signal peaks, so the voltage available at pin 6 drops, due to the internal resistance of the battery. This causes a signal to become, in effect, superimposed on the 9 V battery supply. The decoupling capacitor, C_3, acts as an electronic shock absorber. Due to its energy storage capacity, it smooths out these voltage fluctuations, thus decoupling the signal from the power supply voltage. If this were not done, the battery source would feed signal back into the amplifier. This would cause all sorts of internal resonance, which would cause distortion and increase background noise, and which could even make the amplifier unstable.

Because C_3 is not an electrolytic capacitor, it is not polarized. Connections can, therefore, be made in any polarity.

List of Components

1	Cabinet
1	8-pin dual-in-line package (DIP) IC socket
1	386 audio power amplifier IC
1	10 kΩ potentiometer (log or audio taper)
2	680 kΩ resistors (½ W)
1	100 kΩ resistor (½ W)
1	Nonpolarized capacitor (1 μF, 100 V)
1	Electrolytic capacitor (1,000 μF, 12 V)
1	Nonpolarized capacitor (0.2 μF approximately, 16 V)
1	Low-voltage mini switch (SPST or SPDT)

1   General purpose printed circuit board (PCB)

1   Small loudspeaker

1   Phone jack ($\frac{1}{4}$-inch, mono)

1   Roll hook-up wire (20 gauge, solid)

1   9 V battery (MN 1604 or equivalent)

1   Battery holder

1   Battery connector

Construction Procedure

The first step is to lay out the position of the loudspeaker, potentiometer, and switch on top of the cabinet, and mark the fixing holes. Drill sound vent holes in the area that will be covering the speaker cone.

Lay out and mark fixing holes for the printed circuit board (PCB), battery holder, and input jack in the cabinet. The construction of the PCB can then begin.

There is always at least one copper bus running the entire length of the board. Assign one of these as the ground and connect all grounds to this bus.

The heart of the circuit is the amplifier IC. All PCBs are designed to accept the pin spacing of this chip. The IC holder must be soldered in first, and the chip plugged in after the pins have cooled. Start with the IC holder, because all other components are related to its pin layout.

There is a channel in the center of the board, with conductors on each side designed to accept this IC holder. Notice that there is a semicircular notch and/or a spot at one end of the chip and holder. This identifies pin 1 so that the pin-out can be correctly identified and the chip is not inserted back to front.

All components and wiring must be situated on top of the PCB (that is, on the plastic surface). Wire connections should extend through the holes, and are then soldered onto the copper conductors underneath. Excess wire is cut off.

The holes along each edge of the PCB are designed as access points. All input/output flexible wires should terminate at these edges, never in the center of the board. Solid hook-up wire can then connect to the appropriate component, if no copper conductor is available.

A spacer should be threaded on the fixing screws under each corner of the PCB. This avoids bending and breaking the corners of the board while the fixing screws are being tightened.

Once the wiring is completed, it is a good idea to test for correct voltage polarity at pins 6 and 4 of the IC holder. Remove the chip first, because wrong polarity here will destroy the chip.

Mixer Construction

It is not difficult to construct a 4-channel mixer based on an op-amp used as a summing amplifier. The theory behind a summing op-amp is described in Chapter 3. The circuit to be employed is shown in Figure 10-6.

It is suggested that a 741 op-amp be used. This is one of the most common and best op-amps. It is designed for line-level signal voltages of about 0 dBv, which is suitable for signal processing stages. It is also designed to be energized by a bipolar power supply, which is one that supplies two oppositely polarized voltages, equally balanced on each side of ground. The three power supply terminals are then at voltages such as $+12$ V, ground, and -12 V. This simplifies the amplifier circuit, because the signal can then oscillate in both directions about this zero potential, without having to pass internal capacitors. However, this op-amp can operate equally well at somewhat lower or higher voltages, provided they are bipolar.

With a little ingenuity, we can use the 12 V unipolar power supply illustrated in Figure 10-3 to power this circuit. Our unipolar power supply can easily be adapted to supply $+6$ V and -6 V balanced on either side of ground, and it will then power the mixer satisfactorily.

All we have to do is change the zero ground reference point from the minus terminal of the power supply to the new ground potential half way between the two output terminals. This is done by means of a voltage divider formed by R_1 and R_2 in the schematic of Figure 10-6A. Note that the newly formed ground between the two resistors must be connected to all other grounds in the schematic by means of a ground bus. It must *not* be connected to the black terminal of the power supply, which is now the -6 V source. The two decoupling capacitors, C_5 and C_6, also help to maintain the stability of this new ground. They act as energy reservoirs, countering any tendency of the newly formed ground to shift polarity in either direction.

The potentiometers in the mixer act as input faders or gain controls. As described in the *Signal Tracer Construction* section, all audio volume controls must be in the form of logarithmic potentiometers. Therefore, connect the outer terminals correctly, according to the terminal numbers: terminal 1 to ground, terminal 2 to the wiper, and terminal 3 to the signal input from the input capacitors. The use of coupling capacitors C_1 through C_4 and C_7 is advisable to ensure that a DC component from any source doesn't interfere with the operation of the mixer.

The maximum gain of each channel is determined by the ratio of the feedback resistor, R_7, to the input resistor, R_3 through R_6. Signals entering and leaving should both be at the same level, so the overall gain should be unity. However, for best results, the faders should operate normally at about two-thirds of their maximum height. Then there is *headroom* to allow increase of gain by a few dB, as well as to permit fading to any required extent. It is recommended that an extra 6 dB of boost be available to any channel, so the maximum gain has to be 2. (A gain of 2 corresponds to a level gain of $+6$ dB.) This determines the value of the feedback resistor at 200 kΩ; then the gain of any channel can rise to a maximum value given by $200,000/100,000 = 2$.

As was the case with the signal tracer, the coupling capacitors form an HP filter, because they are in series with the input resistor of the following stage. This

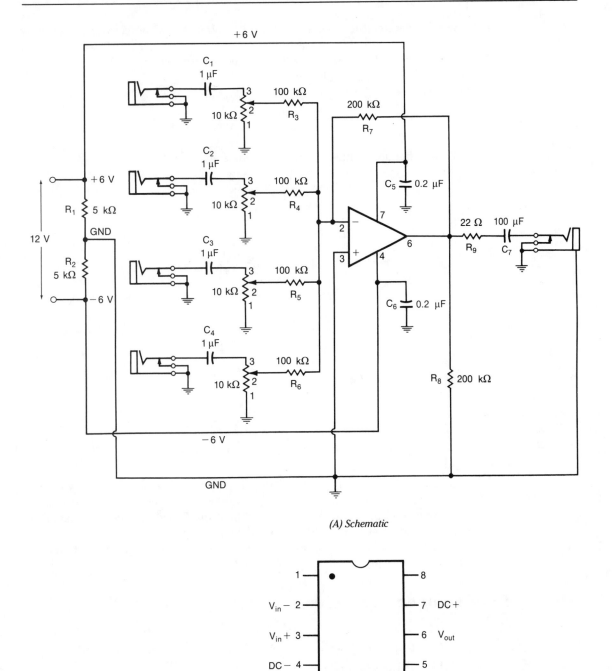

(A) Schematic

(B) IC 741 pin-out

Fig. 10-6 4-channel mixer

mixer is designed to feed an amplifier or other signal processing stage whose input resistance must be at least 600 Ω, but is probably far more. Taking the worst possible case of 600 Ω at the lowest audible frequency of 15 Hz, the output capacitor, C_7, can be evaluated by

$$X_C = \frac{1}{2\pi fC}$$

At break frequency, below which all signals are cut off,

$$X_C = R$$

so,

$$R = \frac{1}{2\pi fC}$$

and

$$C = \frac{1}{2\pi fR}$$

Substituting 15 Hz for f and 600 Ω for R,

$$C = \frac{1}{2\pi \times 15 \times 600}$$

$$= 18 \times 10^{-6} \text{ farads} \approx 20 \ \mu F$$

This gives a loss of 3 dB. Because we wish to lose only about 1 dB, we will use a 100 μF capacitor for C_7.

Notice that the input capacitors feed high 10 kΩ loads, so their reactance can be much higher. This permits 1 μF for the input capacitors.

R_8 acts as a ground resistor. It should equal R_f to balance any DC component that might develop, but its value is not critical.

List of Components

1	Cabinet
1	8-pin DIP socket
1	741 op-amp IC
4	10 kΩ potentiometers (log or audio taper)
2	5 kΩ resistors (½ W)
4	100 kΩ resistors (½ W)

2	200 kΩ resistors (½ W)
1	22 Ω resistor (½ W)
4	Nonpolarized capacitors (1 μF, 12 V)
2	Nonpolarized capacitors (0.2 μF approximately, 16 V)
1	Electrolytic capacitor (100 μF, 16 V)
1	General purpose printed circuit board
5	Phone jacks (¼-inch, mono)

Construction Procedure

After passing the power supply cable through the access hole, the cable should be anchored inside the cabinet, so that an external pull does not apply force to its junction with the PCB.

The next step is the PCB construction. The rules for PCB use that were applicable during the signal tracer construction should always be followed. Position the IC holder across the center channel of the PCB, so that each of its pins contacts a separate conductor. The PCB is designed for compatibility with an IC spanning the center channel.

First, consider the connections to pins 2 and 6. There are five connections to pin 2 and three to pin 6. Because a general purpose PCB normally accommodates only two connection holes for each pin, an alternate connection procedure is needed. It is suggested that, of the two full-length bus conductors on the PCB, one should be assigned as the ground bus. The other should be cut in half, using a razor or sharp knife. It is a good idea to make two cuts close together and remove the piece of copper between them. Use the half of this bus on the pin 1 side as the input bus. Use the other half as connection to pin 6. Connect the input bus to pin 2, using a *short* length of hook-up wire. Use some of its remaining holes to accept the five resistors assigned to pin 2—namely, R_3, R_4, R_5, R_6, and R_7.

I mentioned that a short wire is needed from the input bus to pin 2. This is because pin 2 is sensitive to interference, so only short wire lengths should be assigned to it.

Once these two priority connections have been made, other connections can be assigned to any remaining conductors as seems appropriate. As was suggested during construction of the signal tracer, test for correct power supply voltage and polarity at pins 4 and 7 before plugging in the IC chip. Incorrectly applied polarity here will destroy the chip.

In rotary potentiometers, there is a metal lug on the body casing that extends forward, parallel to the shaft. Do not leave this lug in position without special arrangements. It is intended that a very small hole be drilled to accommodate this lug when the potentiometer is being installed. The purpose is to prevent rotation of the body of the potentiometer by excessive torque applied to the knob. If you do not want to drill this additional hole, do not leave the lug in position, because it will tilt the potentiometer out of true when its fixing nut is tightened. Bend the lug back or break it off with pliers; then the potentiometer will sit flush with the side of the cabinet. In this case, however, it is a good idea to insert a toothed washer between the body of the potentiometer and the cabinet. The teeth will prevent rotation of the potentiometer during use and will serve the same purpose as the lug was intended to serve.

Additional Pre-amplifier Stages

This mixer is designed to accept line-level signals of about 0 dBv, such as would be available from the line output of a tape machine or equalizer. If you want to feed microphone signals to the mixer, additional pre-amplifier stages are needed. It is comparatively easy to construct pre-amplifier stages for this purpose, but a larger cabinet is needed to accommodate the extra printed circuit board. It is a good idea to use dual 741 op-amps. These consist of two op-amps on a single chip. One set of power supply pins is used to power both amplifiers. Two dual 741 op-amps can supply microphone input facilities to all four channels.

By use of a non-inverting amplifier circuit (described in Chapter 3) and a low-voltage slider switch, each pre-amp can be controlled to give either a gain of 50 or a gain of 1 (suitable for line-level inputs). This enables each channel to accept either microphone or line inputs at the flick of a switch. The circuit schematic for a mic pre-amplifier stage is shown in Figure 10-7.

Additional components needed for two pre-amp stages are listed below. Note that the two op-amps on the chip are labeled A and B. I have indicated the pin numbers that should be used for the B amplifier in parentheses on the single schematic. Pins 8 and 4 are common to both op-amps on one chip.

Additional Components Needed for Two Pre-amps

1	8-pin DIP socket
1	Dual 741 op-amp IC
1	General purpose printed circuit board
2	10 kΩ resistors (½ W)
4	500 kΩ resistors (½ W)
2	Nonpolarized capacitors (1 μF, 16 V)
4	Nonpolarized capacitors (0.2 μF, 16 V)
2	Low-voltage switches (SPDT or SPST)

If you prefer to use balanced line microphone cables, use the circuit in Figure 10-8 instead of that in Figure 10-7. In this case, a ¼-inch stereo input jack must be used. In addition, two 10 kΩ resistors, a 500 kΩ resistor, and a 1 μF capacitor are needed for each unit. Also, a DPDT (double pole, double throw) switch is required instead of the SPDT switch specified for the circuit in Figure 10-7.

This balanced input circuit has several advantages over that in Figure 10-7. Both the Mic input and Line input can accommodate balanced lines. This notice-

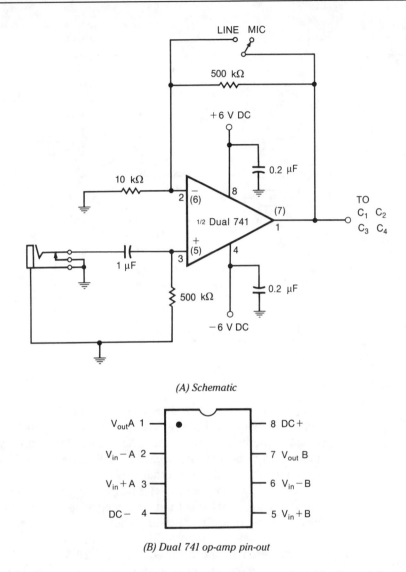

Fig. 10-7
Microphone
pre-amplifier with
Mic/Line switch

(A) Schematic

(B) Dual 741 op-amp pin-out

ably reduces noise interference. If you want to use an unbalanced line, it is completely compatible. By plugging in a mono phone plug instead of a stereo plug, the mono sleeve automatically shorts the non-inverting input to ground. The amplifier then functions as an inverting amplifier with unbalanced input.

Technical Considerations

It is clear that a combination of theoretical knowledge combined with practical skill is needed to solve the sorts of problems that often occur when using audio

Fig. 10-8
Balanced input
mic pre-amplifier
with Mic/Line
switch

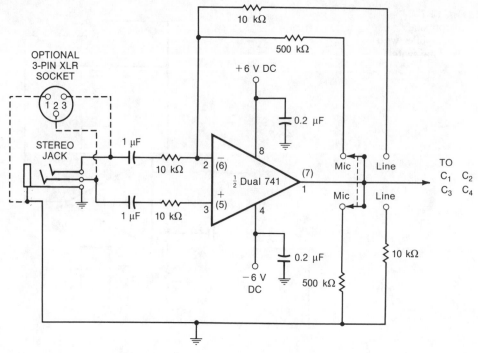

equipment. The best way to acquire these practical skills is to build and test simple audio components. I strongly recommend that you build one or more of the circuits described in this chapter. Not only will the component be useful, but more importantly, the hands-on practice will develop skills and understanding that cannot be achieved in any other way.

One of the most necessary skills is good soldering technique. Bad soldering causes more problems than anything else when constructing or repairing electronic circuits. The following points should be noted.

When soldering onto a printed circuit board, a small, precision 12 or 14 W soldering iron should be used, never a 25 W iron. Use light-duty rosin-cored solder, never normal-duty solder. Keep the tip of the soldering iron sharply pointed and completely coated with solder at all times. When the iron is used for the first time, coat the top with solder as soon as it is hot enough. This prevents corrosion. If any part of the tip becomes brown due to corrosion, unplug the iron and use a small, fine-toothed file to clean the surface. Reheat the iron and coat the tip with a layer of solder before it can become corroded again.

Have a roll of desoldering braid handy. If a conductor becomes shorted by an oversize lump of solder, use desoldering braid to suck up the liquid solder and remake the joint. The technique for using desoldering braid is to lay the end of the braid over the solder to be removed. Press the soldering iron tip down onto the braid, so that the heat goes through the braid and melts the solder underneath.

The braid will then soak up the solder like a sponge. Remove the braid and cut off the solder-covered end. Repeat the process until all excess solder is removed.

Beware of making dry joints. This is the most important point. The newcomer to soldering naturally imagines that the soldering iron and solder should be applied to the wire that is to be soldered, and that the solder can then be spread to the soldering tag on each side of the wire. This is wrong and an almost sure way to make a dry joint.

A dry joint looks like a good joint, but the connection is intermittent. This is because, when the solder was liquid (melted), it didn't *wet* one of the two pieces of metal that had to be joined. The solder probably appears to be covering the metal, but it is not fused onto the metal, so the slightest vibration moves the two pieces of metal apart, and an intermittent connection is formed. As you know, intermittent connections can be extremely difficult to find.

When soldering a wire to a tag (or to the copper conductor of a printed circuit board), do not let solder get onto the wire, to start with. Place the soldering iron on the metal tag (or copper conductor) on one side of the wire and heat this for 2 or 3 seconds. Then apply some solder to the tip of the iron and move the tip backward and forward along the metal tag until the solder positively wets the tag. Do the same to the tag on the other side of the wire, heating it first, then applying solder and spreading it with the tip. Finally and only when solder is adhering to the tag on both sides of the wire, move the soldering iron across and in contact with the wire, applying a little more solder, so that the whole joint is heated and liquid together. Then, remove the soldering iron and make sure the wire doesn't move until the solder has solidified. Push and pull the wire to test the joint. If the wire moves relative to the tag, it is a bad joint and needs resoldering.

The reason why the metal tag must be soldered before the wire is that the tag contains more metal than the wire and takes far longer to heat up. If solder is applied first to the wire, it becomes fused onto the wire; at this point, however, the tag is comparatively cold and the solder won't fuse onto it, so a dry joint is produced.

Semiconductors can easily be destroyed by overheating, so special precautions have to be taken. General purpose transistors used for low-power signal processing—such as op-amps and diodes—do not get heated while they are operating. However, transistors and integrated circuits that conduct sizable current flow are constructed with a metal back plate, which is designed to be bolted onto a heat sink. Any semiconductor with such a back plate should be installed with a heat sink to dissipate its heat during operation. Also, the cabinet should contain ventilation slots.

In the power supply circuit illustrated earlier in Figure 10-3A, the voltage regulators are of this nature. Heat sink compound should be applied to the back plate, and the back plate should then be bolted onto a heat sink before installation. The heat sink compound assists thermal conduction. During layout of these components, make sure that the heat sinks cannot touch each other. Each heat sink is electrically connected to its transistor. A short circuit and burnout of the component can result if two heat sinks at different voltages touch each other.

While soldering any semiconductor, precautions should be taken to avoid overheating. A temporary heat sink, consisting of any metal object, should be placed so that it touches the electrode between the semiconductor body and the point where the soldering is taking place. This drains off some of the heat produced by soldering before it reaches the body of the semiconductor. An alligator clip can be temporarily attached for this purpose. Or a small screwdriver might be wedged between the electrodes of a transistor while they are being soldered. As an additional precaution, limit the time spent in soldering any one transistor connection to not more than 4 or 5 seconds. If soldering is not completed by then, leave the joint to cool while other connections are being made. Then spend another 4 or 5 seconds finishing off the soldering. In this way, semiconductors will not be damaged during installation.

11 Troubleshooting and Maintenance

11 Troubleshooting and Maintenance

Audio Chain Troubleshooting

An important ability of an audio engineer is to be able to locate a fault when it occurs, and if possible, to be able to repair it. Excessive time, trouble, and expense result from having to take each piece of faulty equipment to a repairer. In addition, faults often occur in a cable or patch cord, which can easily be misinterpreted as occurring in a component that is, in fact, working perfectly.

Troubleshooting is like solving a detective mystery. The same logical deductive process needs to be used as would be appropriate in a criminal investigation. The method is simple. Narrow down the possible list of suspects until there is only one left—the guilty party. And don't forget to include in your list all cables and patch cords used in the interfaces between components.

Let's take a typical audio chain as an example. We will start with a microphone followed by a mic pre-amp, a line amp, an equalizer, a mixer, a power amp, and ending with a loudspeaker (see Figure 11-1).

Suppose this system is switched on. (On many occasions, components have been said to be "not working" when they were either not plugged in or not switched on. So watch out for this one!) When sound is fed into the microphone, nothing comes out of the loudspeaker. The audio chain can be tested to find the position of the fault, starting from one end and working to the other. It is a simple, step-by-step process.

Troubleshooting Left to Right

If we decide to work from left to right, we need a signal generator feeding the mic pre-amplifier in place of the microphone. This is set to 1 kHz (audio test frequency)

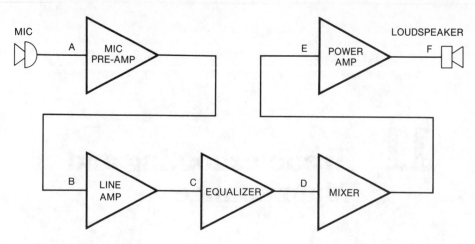

Fig. 11-1 A typical audio chain

at a low output voltage level of about − 35 dBv, equivalent to what a microphone outputs. Also, a signal tracer is needed. This consists of a small, low-power amplifier with a built-in loudspeaker. A signal tracer is easy to make, as described in Chapter 10. It is useful to connect a lead terminated by an alligator clip to the ground input of the signal tracer, and a lead terminated by a probe to the hot lead input. Then the ground can be kept permanently connected to the ground bus of the audio chain, while probing the signal at various interfaces along its path.

Now connect the tracer input to points B, C, D, E, and F in sequence (see Figure 11-1). The stage before the point where the signal disappears is the faulty stage. For instance, suppose a signal is detected at points B and C, but not at point D; this means that the signal is passing through the pre-amp and through the line amp, but failing to pass through the equalizer. It is obvious that the EQ is where the fault lies. Don't assume yet that the fault must be in the EQ itself. Remember the cables. At least 50 percent of all faults occur in cables, not in audio components. So test the interface cable between the line amp and the EQ. Also, test the interface cable from the EQ to the mixer. If both of these cables are good, you can strongly suspect that the EQ is the culprit.

During a professional recording session, it is not possible to make repairs. The procedure then is to find and pull out the faulty component and replace it with a good one. Speed and accuracy in finding the fault and getting the system working again is what is needed. Then, at a convenient time, the faulty component can be repaired.

Troubleshooting Right to Left

I mentioned that the audio chain can be tested either from left to right or from right to left. If we decide to start the troubleshooting from the right, a signal tracer is not needed. Only a signal generator is used. Again, it is useful to have a cable with the ground output from the signal generator terminated by an alligator clip and the hot lead terminated by a probe. The idea is to inject a signal (of suitable voltage) at points E, D, C, B, and A in sequence, until the point is found where no signal output is heard from the loudspeaker. The component to the right of this point must be the faulty one.

But there is a catch. The output from the signal generator has insufficient power to drive the loudspeaker audibly. Therefore, the sequence of events has to start with a test of the loudspeaker. To do this, disconnect the speaker from the power amplifier. Use the multimeter or FET meter to measure resistance on the R × 1 range, and connect the meter probes to the loudspeaker terminals. If the speaker makes an audible click when the probes are connected, and another click when the probes are disconnected, then the speaker is good. If there is no click, and the meter reads infinitely high resistance, the voice coil is open circuit and the speaker is not working. (The same method can be used to test a dynamic microphone, but in this case, it is advisable to set the meter to the R × 1 kΩ range.)

If the speaker is working, reconnect it to the audio chain and proceed with the test by injecting the audio signal at points E, D, C, B, and A in sequence. Note that the signal voltage level to be injected anywhere along the audio chain should be at about 0 dBv—that is, about 0.8 V. However, at the input of the pre-amplifier, the injected signal should be about − 35 dBv, which is about 15 mV.

There is one other improvement that can speed up this method of troubleshooting. Start by injecting the signal at the mid-point of the audio chain, instead of at one end. If the signal is injected at point D as a first step, and if it is heard coming out of the loudspeaker, it means that all stages following point D are working, and the fault must lie to the left. Then proceed to points C, B, and A in sequence. If no signal is heard from injection at point D, then the fault follows this point; proceed to points E and F in sequence. This is the quickest possible way to locate a faulty stage.

Cable Testing

I mentioned that often a suspected cable or patch cord has to be tested. The method is this. Set the multimeter to measure resistance on the R × 1 range. With both ends of the cable held close to each other, connect the probes of the meter to the two ground connections, one at each end of the cable. The meter should read less than 1 ohm. Then connect the meter probes to the two hot lead terminations. Again, the meter should read less than 1 ohm. If there are three conductors, a continuity test like this should be applied to all three conductors. If, in any case, the meter reads infinitely high resistance, that particular conductor is open circuit.

Next, test for short circuits on any of the cable terminations between ground and each of the hot leads in turn. The meter should read infinitely high resistance. If it reads 1 ohm or less, there is a short circuit.

Electronic Circuit Troubleshooting

A method similar to audio chain troubleshooting can be used when troubleshooting an electronic circuit, such as an amplifier or mixer. First, check to see that the DC power supply voltages are present. Then, to find the faulty stage, scan the signal path either from input to output or from output to input, as was done in the audio chain troubleshooting procedure.

The test equipment needed is the same—namely, an audio signal generator, a signal tracer (optional but useful), and an AC/DC VTVM or FET meter. When scanning from input to output, inject a signal at the input and use the signal tracer to probe for this signal at various places along the signal path. The point where the signal is lost identifies the faulty stage. Alternatively, with an amplifier or signal tracer connected to the output, inject a signal at various stages from output to input. It is useful to have a manufacturer's schematic diagram available. This helps to identify the signal path. It also provides information on the correct quiescent voltages at the transistor terminals.

When the faulty stage has been found, use the FET meter or VTVM to measure the DC voltages (under quiescent conditions) at the terminals of the transistor. This should give a clue as to the fault. If the power supply voltage is missing, find the break in the supply line. If power is present but other voltages are faulty, it may be that the transistor needs replacing. By measuring the voltage drop across a resistor, the current flow can be found. Thus, it is always possible to find out if a transistor is conducting; just find the current through its emitter resistor. Theoretical understanding is necessary, but as in learning to ride a bicycle, there is no substitute for practice.

Intermittent Faults

The most difficult faults to find are the intermittent faults. You know Murphy's Law on intermittent faults: "When the equipment is being tested, it works perfectly. Only when it is replaced in its cabinet or put back into service does it immediately stop working."

In the case of cable testing, it is a good idea to wiggle the ends of the cable while testing for continuity or short circuits. Bending the cable near its connectors might disconnect a loose connection, while bending in the other direction might give an illusion of continuity.

The only other advice I can give about intermittent faults is gently to kick, joggle, or tap on components or wired connections. If a click or crackle is heard, that is a clue. When working inside an electrical circuit that is powered, use an insulated rod, such as a ballpoint pen sleeve with the refill removed. With this, gently tap all wires and components until one clicks or crackles when tapped. This may lead to a dry joint or some other loose connection that might be the cause of the intermittent fault.

Power Supply Troubleshooting

The action of a power supply was described in Chapter 10; from this it is easy to apply the overall troubleshooting method if power supply failure should occur.

However, before talking about dealing with a power supply that has completely died, I need to mention a common problem that is more subtle in its effects.

It sometimes happens that a 60 Hz or 120 Hz line frequency hum is heard superimposed on the audio signal. There are several possible causes. One lies in the power supply—especially if the equipment is old—and results from partial failure of a smoothing capacitor.

When an electrolytic capacitor gets old, some of its electrolyte might dry out. Or the capacitor might start to leak its charge internally. Either of these faults is capable of reducing capacitance. The drying out of electrolyte means that a smaller area of plate is charged. A leaking of charge means that the time during which a charge is held is reduced, so the capacitor reacts just as a smaller one would.

If this happens to the smoothing capacitor, the AC ripple increases in amplitude, and the loss of voltage between peaks causes the troughs of the ripple to descend to a value below the output level of the regulator. Then a severe ripple is audible in the audio signal.

If the smoothing capacitor is suspect, there is an easy way to check it. Obtain another large electrolytic capacitor. It needs to be of about the same capacitance as the one in the power supply, but its value is not critical. It also needs to have at least the same working voltage. With the line plug removed from the wall socket and the equipment switched off, discharge the existing smoothing capacitor by holding the blade of a screwdriver across its terminals. This will probably cause a flash and a bang. (There is a more civilized way of discharging a capacitor: hold a low value resistor across the terminals. This discharges it in about 2 seconds without a bang.)

Connect your spare capacitor temporarily in parallel with the one in the power supply. An easy way to make a temporary connection is to use two flexible insulated wires terminated by alligator clips. Watch out for two things. Electrolytic capacitors are polarized. The positive terminal of the capacitor must be connected to the more positive terminal of the circuit; so make sure that the temporary capacitor is connected with the same polarity as the one in the circuit. The other precaution, already mentioned, is that the DC working voltage of your temporary capacitor must be equal to or greater than the one in the circuit. With connections complete, switch on and see if the hum is reduced or eliminated. If it is, the problem can be solved by replacing the old capacitor with a new one. After the test is completed, switch off and discharge the capacitors as before. Then remove the temporary capacitor.

If complete failure of the power supply should occur, it is easy to find the fault and make the necessary repairs. As a first step in all troubleshooting, make a visual inspection of the circuitry. Look for any wires that have come adrift, or any blackened or burnt components. Also, test all fuses for continuity. If a blown fuse is found, don't just replace it. The cause of the failure also needs to be corrected. Replace any fuse with the correct current rating or it will be worthless.

The next step is to work through the circuit from left to right, just as was suggested in the previous section. However, now we are looking for electrical power, not an audio signal, so a voltmeter is all that we need. The discovery of a faulty voltage instantly indicates where the problem lies. Knowledge of the theory behind a power supply circuit will tell you what voltages should be present at the various stages from source to output.

Starting from the left, there should be 115 AC volts across the transformer primary. There should be a few more AC volts than the power supply's rated output across the secondary. (For instance, a 15 V power supply should have about 18 AC volts across its secondary.) At the output of the rectifier, which is most readily accessed across the terminals of the smoothing capacitor, there should be roughly the same voltage, but now it should be DC rather than AC. At the output terminals, there should be the rated voltage. If the final voltage is too high, the regulator needs replacing. If, at any point, the voltage is zero, the component to the left is the faulty one.

Tape Recorder Alignment

For tape recorder alignment the following equipment is needed:

- Denatured alcohol and cotton swabs
- Head demagnetizer
- VTVM or FET meter or good-quality multimeter
- NAB test tape
- Signal generator

Cleaning and Demagnetizing

Before a recording is made and before any alignment is carried out, the heads and tape guides should be cleaned and demagnetized. Demagnetization is particularly important before the test tape is threaded, because a residual magnetism on the heads will partially erase the high-frequency test tones. If that should happen, the test tape will no longer be useable as a reference guide.

Cleaning is best carried out with denatured alcohol on a cotton swab. Wipe over the surface of the heads, tape guides, capstan, and pinch roller. Clean up any surplus alcohol with the dry end of the swab.

Next, use a head demagnetizer. This consists of a 115 AC line voltage transformer with an extended core. Some have a switch button that has to be depressed while in use. Others are energized as soon as they are plugged in. These should not be left plugged in when not in use. The demagnetizing process is as follows:

1. Make sure the tape recorder is switched off; otherwise, the high magnetic flux applied to the heads could burn out the head pre-amplifier.

2. With the demagnetizer held in the on position, bring the metal end close to each head surface and tape guide in turn.

3. Move the demagnetizer slowly at all times. The demagnetizing process requires slow movement away from the object in order to demagnetize it.

4. *Never* switch off the demagnetizer until it is at least 2 feet away from the parts being demagnetized. If this should happen, repeat the demagnetization over again.

5. Keep the demagnetizer away from all magnetic tapes.

The need for slow movement away from the object being demagnetized results from the fact that the alternating magnetic field produced by the demagnetizer is strong. It magnetically saturates the object, first with one polarity, then with the other. As it moves slowly away, its field becomes progressively weaker. Consequently, each reversal of field not only cancels the previously induced magnetic polarity, but produces a slightly weaker opposite polarity. It is this gradual reduction in strength of each oppositely produced polarity that eventually produces complete demagnetization. A sudden movement away from the object, or a switching off of the demagnetizer close to the object, is likely to leave it more strongly magnetized than it was before.

It might be well to note at this point that the erase head on the tape deck works in a similar way. An amplified value of the high-frequency bias voltage is used to energize the erase head. This head is placed before the record head. In the record mode, the strongly amplified bias voltage is applied to the erase head and it magnetically saturates the tape as it passes over the erase head. As the tape moves farther and farther from the erase head, the opposing polarities become progressively weaker, so that when the tape arrives at the record head, it is completely demagnetized and ready for its new recording.

Basic Alignment Procedure

Depending on the sophistication of the tape recorder, alignment might occupy only a few steps or many. In the case of a simple machine, with no facilities for reproduce or record equalization, the recommended steps are these.

After cleaning and demagnetizing, *check the playback level of the test tones* on the NAB test tape. Connect an AC voltmeter to the line output (or if there is none, to the loudspeaker terminals) with a suitable loudspeaker load. A loudspeaker is necessary in any case, in order to hear the specified frequency of each test tone.

With the machine in reproduce mode, play the first tone. This is normally a *reference level tone* at the standard test frequency of either 1 kHz or 700 Hz. Adjust the gain to register 0 dB on the VU meter, or 0 dBv at the line output, or 5 or 10 dBv at the loudspeaker output terminals. In this case, subtract 5 or 10 dB from all output readings.

The next tone on the test tape is 15 kHz. It is for *azimuth alignment*. Azimuth is the angle between the line formed by the head gap and the direction of tape travel. The head gap should be perpendicular to the edge of the tape. Because high frequencies are so closely packed, their response falls off rapidly if there is any azimuth error. Therefore, azimuth is always set and checked at the highest frequency of 15 kHz. (The position of the azimuth setting screw for each head should be indicated in the manufacturer's manual.)

Play the 15 kHz test tone and note its level on the output voltmeter or VU meter. Then turn the azimuth setting screw very slowly, first one way, then the other. The azimuth should be set to give maximum output at 15 kHz. There are sometimes a number of false peaks at various azimuth settings. The correct setting is the peak that gives the highest output of the various peaks that may occur.

Once the azimuth has been accurately set, it should not be necessary to reset or check it frequently. (Equalization checks should be done more often, however,) Some operators like to seal the azimuth setting screw with a dab of paint between the side of the screw and its surrounding surface. This prevents the screw from working loose as a result of vibrations.

Next on the test tape, follow a sequence of test tones from 12 kHz down to about 50 Hz, each about 15 seconds. Tabulate each frequency and output level. If the reproduce equalizer is functioning correctly, the levels should all be within about 2 dB of the 1 kHz reference level. If they are a little less accurate than this, it is not important, as long as you know what they are. It is a good idea to plot a graph of the reproduce frequency response level plotted vertically on a frequency base scaled logarithmically. Keep this for reference. Then, if there is any sudden change, such as a fall-off of high frequencies, you will know that some corrective action is needed.

Although a simply made consumer tape recorder does not allow you to alter the equalization of the record system, the record characteristics need to be known. In this way, recordings can be made as compatible with standard NAB specifications as possible.

One of the most important things to understand about tape recording is the significance of *bias voltage*. An increase in bias tends to reduce distortion and background noise, but it also reduces the high-frequency recording response. So the operator has to make a trade-off between improved signal-to-noise ratio and loss of high frequencies.

A good guide with which to start is 3 dB over bias at 10 kHz. This is described in detail later. Many consumer machines have no facilities for adjusting bias. It is then necessary to choose a tape whose bias requirements allow satisfactory recording performance. By always using the same tape, consistent results can be ensured. These can be established in the overall record/reproduce test described next. Some machines have a bias level switch that can give either high bias or low bias. Use the low bias setting for tapes specified as requiring normal bias. Tapes that require high bias should only be used on machines that have a high bias facility or adjustable bias.

To carry out the *overall record/reproduce test*, start by removing the test tape from the machine and replacing it with a blank tape. Feed to the line input a 1 kHz signal from the signal generator set at + 4 dBv. (This is specified as + 4 dBm, but assuming a standard load, equals + 4 dBv.) Adjust the record level to give − 10 dB on the VU meter. (It is wise to test record 7½ ips tapes at − 10 dB. This lets you add the required degree of pre-emphasis to the HF tones without over-saturation of the tape.) Keeping the record gain unchanged and maintaining exactly the same input voltage at all frequencies, record about 10 seconds, first of the 1 kHz reference frequency, then of all other frequencies that are included on the test tape.

After recording is complete, rewind and play back your test recording. During the 1 kHz reference tone, adjust the output gain to obtain 0 dBv at the line output, or the same 5 or 10 dBv that was measured at the loudspeaker terminals. Then tabulate the output level at each frequency and plot the overall response graph. This gives a comprehensive view of the tape recorder's characteristics.

For best compatibility of recording performance, the overall record/ reproduce graph should not necessarily be flat. It should coincide as far as possible with the playback characteristics of the NAB test tape. To the extent that it does so, your recordings will be perfect when reproduced according to the NAB standards on any high-quality machine. Once it is known where any discrepancy lies, it is often possible to counteract this during a recording session. But it is necessary first to have good information about your equipment.

Professional Alignment Procedure

The alignment procedure for professional tape machines involves a somewhat different approach. The difference results from the fact that these machines have separate record and replay heads, with user-adjustable equalization for both record and replay amplifiers. They also incorporate user-adjustable bias voltage. The method of cleaning and demagnetizing is exactly the same as previously described. This must always be carried out as a first step.

Before continuing to describe the alignment procedure, I must mention that there is a difference between using a 7½ ips test tape and a 15 ips test tape. With a 15 ips tape, all frequencies are recorded at operational level, which is normally 250 nanowebers/meter. This should be calibrated at 0 dB on the VU meter. In the 7½ ips test tape, the reference level and frequency test tones are all recorded at − 10 dB. This avoids the risk of overload distortion at high frequencies, during which increased pre-emphasis is applied. At the end of these test tapes there is normally a reference frequency recording at operational level, 0 dB. This can be used as a final verification of operational level, if required. At each step in the following alignment procedure, the correct level settings for 15 ips machines are indicated, followed by the corresponding values for 7½ ips machines in parentheses.

First, *align the reproduce system* by replaying the test tape. At the reference tone of 1 kHz, adjust the reproduce level to obtain 0 dB (− 10 dB) on the VU meter. Next comes the azimuth setting tone. Set the playback head azimuth as previously described.

The various frequency tones follow, each usually about 15 seconds long. Use a high-frequency tone of about 12 kHz to adjust the HF reproduce equalizer and set the output level to that of the reference tone. Then replay the reference tone and reset the output to 0 dB (– 10 dB) once again, in case the adjustment has caused any change in the reference value. Use the reproduce level control for this purpose.

Next, wind on until a tone of about 100 Hz occurs. Use this to adjust the LF reproduce equalizer to reproduce the correct reference level of 0 dB (– 10 dB) for this LF recording. Again, reset the original 1 kHz reference tone to 0 dB (– 10 dB) by use of the reproduce level control. (Only on the 7½ ips test tape, there follows a final reference tone recorded at operational level, 0 dB. This enables you to make any final adjustment to the reproduce level to obtain exactly 0 dB on the VU meter.)

Now that the reproduce equalizer has been aligned for both HF and LF reproduction, it is time to replay all of the frequency tones in sequence without any further adjustment. Tabulate each frequency against its output level and plot these on semi-log graph paper—the level vertically against a frequency base scaled in octaves. This completes the reproduce equalization. It should be flat with 2 dB.

The next step is to *align the record characteristics*. Before doing anything else, remove the test tape and exchange it for a blank tape ready for recording.

This type of sophisticated recorder has two great advantages over the consumer model. First, the bias voltage is adjustable. Because every type and make of tape requires a different bias, any tape can be used to its best advantage by using the optimum bias for that particular tape. Remember that once the bias has been set, it is not necessarily valid for any other type of tape.

The other advantage is that the recording can be monitored direct from the tape while it is being recorded. The sequence of heads is erase, record, replay; so what has been recorded can be monitored through headphones a fraction of a second later, as the tape passes over the replay head.

The alignment of the record stage has to follow these steps. First, *set the record head azimuth*. With blank tape threaded, connect a signal generator to the line input. Adjust it to supply + 4 dBv at 15 kHz. Run the machine in the record mode, with the record level set to produce 0 dB (– 10 dB) on the VU meter.

Adjust the azimuth setting screw of the *record* head (not the replay head). As you turn this azimuth screw first one way and then the other, the record head azimuth is altered. It is only when it is identical with the replay azimuth that maximum signal output occurs. This can be read from the VU meter. The correct setting occurs when the output VU meter reads maximum value.

Now *find the optimum bias value* for this particular tape. Adjust the signal generator to output 10 kHz at the same level. Run the machine in the record mode and turn the bias control fully counterclockwise, so that the bias voltage falls to zero. Gradually turn up the bias voltage, watching the replay level on the output VU meter. As the bias increases, the level of the recorded signal will increase until a point is reached where it stops increasing and starts to fall as the bias continues to rise. Reduce the bias until the maximum output is again found and note this value. Continue to increase the bias until the output has fallen by 3 dB below its maximum value. This is one method of finding the optimum bias for this tape. It is called 3 dB over bias at 10 kHz. Other bias setting methods can be used. It is useful to consult the tape manufacturer's literature to find its recommended bias setting procedure.

Now that the record head azimuth and bias voltage have been correctly aligned, it is possible to *align the equalization* of the record amplifier. Refer back to the circuit configuration in Figure 8-4; it will help you understand the significance of the following steps. Set the signal generator to the reference frequency of 1 kHz. Ensure that its output level remains constant at + 4 dBv at all frequencies. Run the tape recorder in the record mode and adjust the record level to produce 0 dB (– 10 dB) on the VU meter. (It is assumed that the reproduce level control remains at the operating level established during reproduce alignment.)

Now set the signal generator to a high frequency of about 12 kHz (keeping its output at + 4 dBv), and adjust the HF record equalizer until the replay level is 0 dB (– 10 dB) on the VU meter. Return the signal generator to the reference frequency of 1 kHz and recheck that the recording produces 0 dB (– 10 dB) on the VU meter. Readjust the record level control slightly, if necessary, to obtain this.

Next, set the signal generator to a low frequency of about 100 Hz and adjust the LF record equalizer to obtain 0 dB (– 10 dB) on the VU meter. Recheck the reference frequency of 1 kHz for 0 dB (– 10 dB) replay, adjusting the record level slightly, if necessary. The record equalization is now complete.

Step the signal generator through all of the frequencies listed in the test tape and note the resulting level of each recorded frequency, as indicated on the reproduce VU meter. Tabulate and plot the results of the overall record/ reproduce response. This graph should closely coincide with the replay responses from the NAB test tape. You will then know that the recording characteristics will give excellent results when reproduced on any good-quality NAB machine.

In the case of 7½ ips machines, an additional step is necessary. With the signal generator at reference frequency and + 4 dBv, make a recording, increasing the recording level until 0 dB is obtained on the VU meter. This aligns the record level control to the correct operating level.

If there is a record calibrate control, a further step is needed. This record calibrate alignment is the same for both 15 and 7½ ips speeds. Make an additional recording of 1 kHz reference frequency with the signal generator at the usual + 4 dBv. Now switch the VU meter to *Input* (switch A in Figure 8-4) and adjust the record calibrate level to obtain 0 dB on the VU meter. Switch back to *Reproduce*. The meter should read the same.

If there is a sync facility, next align the sync level. Switch off the signal generator and wind back some of the tape that you have just recorded at reference level. Play back this tape. With switches A and B (both operated by a single switch—refer back to Figure 8-4) in the *Sync* position, adjust the sync level to obtain 0 dB on the VU meter. The meter should now read the same in both the Sync and Reproduce positions. This completes the alignment of the tape machine.

A Formulas and Derivations

A Formulas and Derivations

Output Voltage of Differential Amplifiers

(See *Differential Amplifiers* in Chapter 3.)

The formula for finding the output voltage of a differential op-amp can be derived as follows. First, find the outputs for each separate input voltage. Let us call the output from V_1, V_{L1}, and that from input V_2, V_{L2}. Superimposing them gives the total output voltage (refer to Figure 3-8).

1. Output due to V_1

$$V_{L1} = V_1 \, G_V$$

But,

$$G_V = \frac{R_f}{R_i} \qquad \text{(for an inverting op-amp).}$$

So,

$$V_{L1} = -V_1 \frac{R_f}{R_i} \qquad \text{(A-1)}$$

(The negative sign is due to the inverting character of this input.)

2. Output due to V_2

$$V_{L2} = V_2' G_V$$

But,

$$G_V = 1 + \frac{R_f}{R_i} \qquad \text{(for a non-inverting op-amp)},$$

or

$$G_V = \frac{R_i + R_f}{R_i}$$

So,

$$V_{L2} = V_2{}'\left(\frac{R_i + R_f}{R_i}\right) \qquad \text{(A-2)}$$

However, $V_2{}'$ is the voltage at the op-amp itself. Its value in terms of the applied voltage, V_2 has to be found. Between V_2 and ground there are two resistors—R_i and R_g—forming a voltage divider. From the Voltage Proportionality Law, we know that

$$\frac{V_2{}'}{R_g} = \frac{V_2}{R_i + R_g}$$

So,

$$V_2{}' = V_2\left(\frac{R_g}{R_i + R_g}\right)$$

But,

$$R_g = R_f$$

so this equation can be written

$$V_2{}' = V_2\left(\frac{R_f}{R_i + R_f}\right)$$

Substituting this expression for $V_2{}'$ in Equation A-2 gives

$$V_{L2} = V_2\left(\frac{R_f}{R_i + R_f} \times \frac{R_i + R_f}{R_i}\right)$$

Canceling the common term $(R_i + R_f)$ leaves us with

$$V_{L2} = V_2\frac{R_f}{R_i} \qquad \text{(A-3)}$$

The final output voltage can be found by superimposing the two output voltages, V_{L1} and V_{L2}, from Equations A-1 and A-3.

$$V_L = V_2 \frac{R_f}{R_i} - V_1 \frac{R_f}{R_i}$$

Factoring, we get

$$V_L = \frac{R_f}{R_i}(V_2 - V_1)$$

This demonstrates the derivation of Equation 3-2, in Chapter 3.

Output Level of High-Pass Shelving Filter

(See *The Pole/Zero Approach* in Chapter 4.)
   Draw the Bode plot and graph the output level of the high-pass shelving filter in Figure A-1.

Fig. A-1 HP shelving filter

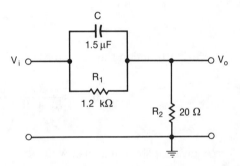

$$\text{Transfer function, } H(S) = \frac{V_o}{V_i} = \frac{Z_o}{Z_i}$$

but

$$Z_o = R_2$$

and

$$Z_i = \frac{R_1(1/SC)}{R_1 + (1/SC)} + R_2$$

Multiplying the numerator and denominator of the fraction by SC, we get

$$Z_i = \frac{R_1}{SR_1C + 1} + R_2$$

So,

$$H(S) = \frac{Z_o}{Z_i} = \frac{R_2}{\dfrac{R_1}{SR_1C + 1} + R_2}$$

Multiplying the numerator and denominator by $(SR_1C + 1)$ produces

$$H(S) = \frac{R_2 (SR_1C + 1)}{SR_1R_2C + R_1 + R_2}$$

Divide out K, the DC gain. (By inspection of the schematic, it can be seen that at zero frequency, the capacitor becomes an open circuit, so the gain is given by the voltage divider formed by the two resistors only.) So, the DC gain is

$$K = \frac{R_2}{R_1 + R_2}$$

The transfer function thus becomes

$$H(S) = \frac{R_2}{R_1 + R_2}\left(\frac{SR_1C + 1}{S\dfrac{R_1R_2C}{R_1 + R_2} + 1}\right) \qquad \text{(A-4)}$$

The equivalent standard form would be

$$H(S) = K\left(\frac{S\mathcal{T}_1 + 1}{S\mathcal{T}_2 + 1}\right) \qquad \text{(A-5)}$$

By comparing Equations A-4 and A-5, it is clear that the coefficients of S are the time constants. So the constants are

$$K = \frac{R_2}{R_1 + R_2} \qquad\qquad \mathcal{T}_1 = R_1C \qquad\qquad \mathcal{T}_2 = \frac{R_1R_2C}{R_1 + R_2}$$

Substituting the actual component values,

$$K = \frac{20}{1200 + 20} = 0.0164 \qquad\qquad T_1 = 1.2 \times 10^3 \times 1.5 \times 10^{-6}$$

$$T_2 = \frac{1.2 \times 10^3 \times 20 \times 1.5 \times 10^{-6}}{1200 + 20}$$

and

$$\text{Level K} = 20 \log 0.0164 \qquad\qquad T_1 = 1.8 \times 10^{-3}\,\text{s}$$

$$T_2 = 2.951 \times 10^{-5}\,\text{s}$$

So level K $= -35.7$ dB.

From these time constants, we see that

$$f_1 = \frac{1}{2\pi T_1} = \frac{1}{2\pi \times 1.8 \times 10^{-3}} = 88.4 \text{ Hz (a zero)}$$

$$f_2 = \frac{1}{2\pi T_2} = \frac{1}{2\pi \times 2.951 \times 10^{-5}} = 5.39 \text{ kHz (a pole)}$$

To construct the Bode plot, start by drawing a vertical dotted line at each break frequency (see Figure A-2). Note that at the lowest limit of frequency (when S = 0), the level is -35.7 dB. So draw a horizontal line at -35.7 dB from the Y-axis until the 88.4 Hz break frequency is reached. This is a zero, so the graph turns up there by 6 dB/octave. A 6 dB/octave slope is simply a straight line that rises (or falls) by 6 dB, for a horizontal displacement of one octave (double the frequency). Continue this slope until the next break frequency is reached at 5.39 kHz. This is a pole, so the graph turns down here by -6 dB/octave, bringing the Bode back to a horizontal straight line. This completes the Bode plot.

For calculation purposes, any $(ST_n + 1)$ term can be replaced by

$$\sqrt{\left(\frac{f}{f_n}\right)^2 + 1}$$

So the standard form of

$$H(S) = K \left(\frac{ST_1 + 1}{ST_2 + 1}\right)$$

becomes

$$H(f) = K \sqrt{\frac{\left(\frac{f}{f_1}\right)^2 + 1}{\left(\frac{f}{f_2}\right)^2 + 1}}$$

Thus, the level change is shown as

$$L_{VG} = 20 \log K \sqrt{\frac{\left(\frac{f}{f_1}\right)^2 + 1}{\left(\frac{f}{f_2}\right)^2 + 1}}$$

Substituting the values for K and the break frequencies,

$$L_{VG} = 20 \log \left(0.0164 \sqrt{\frac{\left(\frac{f}{88.4}\right)^2 + 1}{\left(\frac{f}{5.390}\right)^2 + 1}} \right) \qquad \text{(A-6)}$$

Fig. A-2 HP shelving filter response

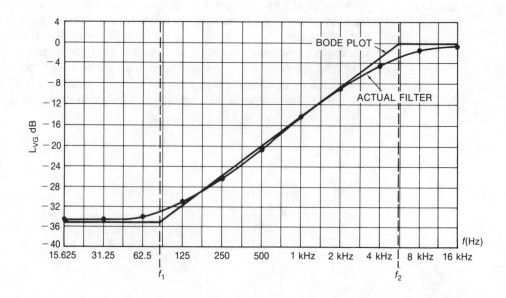

The filter response can now be plotted from Equation A-6 to show the output level at all frequencies. It is suggested that the value be found at each octave within the audible range from 15.625 Hz to 16 kHz. The graphs can be conveniently plotted on a frequency base scaled in octaves, forming a base 2 logarithmic scaled horizontal axis. An HP 11 calculator program can be used to facilitate calculations. After programming, return to the run mode and proceed as follows. For the first run only, initialize with keystrokes **g RTN, 15.625, STO 0**. Then key **f A**. The frequency will be displayed. To find the output level at this frequency, press **R/S**. It is necessary only to key **f A** and **R/S** for each subsequent reading. The frequencies will be incremented in octaves automatically. To repeat the entire sequence, key in **15.625, STO 0**, then **f A** and **R/S**. (The program for this calculation is shown in the box below, along with the response in Table A-1.)

HP 11 Program for Shelving Filter Analysis

Program	Initialization
f Lbl A	g RTN
RCL 0	15.625
R/S	STO 0
88.4	f A
÷	R/S
g x^2	
1	
+	
RCL 0	
5390	
÷	
g x^2	
1	
+	
÷	
$\sqrt{x}$	
.0164	
x	
g log	
20	
x	
STO 1	
RCL 0	
2	
x	
STO 0	
RCL 1	
g RTN	

Table A-1
Shelving filter
response

Frequency (Hz)	L_{VG} dB
25.625	− 35.6
31.25	− 35.2
62.5	− 33.9
125	− 30.9
250	− 26.2
500	− 20.6
1,000	− 14.7
2,000	− 9.2
4,000	− 4.5
8,000	− 1.6
16,000	− 0.5

Output Level of Bandpass Filter

(See *Bandpass Filters* in Chapter 4.)

Draw the Bode plot and graph the output level of the bandpass filter shown in Figure A-3.

Fig. A-3
Bandpass filter

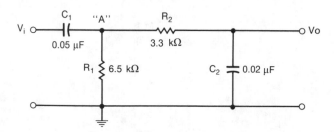

To simplify the process, call the impedance of the network between A and ground, Z_A. This consists of the series connected R_2 and C_2 shunted across R_1 (that is, in parallel with R_1). So,

$$Z_A = \frac{R_1[R_2 + (1/SC_2)]}{R_1 + R_1 + (1/SC_2)}$$

Multiplying the numerator and denominator by SC_2, we get

$$Z_A = \frac{R_1(SR_2C_2 + 1)}{S(R_1 + R_2)C_2 + 1} \qquad \text{(A-7)}$$

The simplified circuit that we are considering now looks like that in Figure A-4.

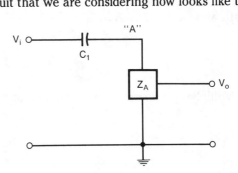

Between V_i and ground there is a simple series circuit, so V_A can be found from

$$V_A = \frac{V_i \, Z_A}{Z_i}$$

where Z_i = total input impedance.

$$V_A = \frac{V_i \, Z_A}{(1/SC_1) + Z_A} \qquad \text{(A-8)}$$

Substituting in Equation A-8 for Z_A from Equation A-7, produces

$$V_A = \frac{\dfrac{V_i R_1 (S R_2 C_2 + 1)}{S(R_1 + R_2)C_2 + 1}}{\dfrac{1}{SC_1} + \dfrac{R_1 \, (S R_2 C_2 + 1)}{S(R_1 + R_2)C_2 + 1}}$$

Adding the two denominator terms by use of a common denominator of $SC_1[S(R_1 + R_2)C_2 + 1]$

$$V_A = \frac{\dfrac{V_i R_1 (S R_2 C_2 + 1)}{S((R_1 + R_2)C_2 + 1}}{\dfrac{S(R_1 + R_2)C_2 + 1 + SC_1 R_1 \, (S R_2 C_2 + 1)}{SC_1[S(R_1 + R_2)C_2 + 1]}}$$

and canceling like terms,

$$V_A = \frac{V_i R_1 (S R_2 C_2 + 1)SC_1}{S(R_1 + R_2)C_2 + 1 + SC_1 R_1 \, (S R_2 C_2 + 1)} \qquad \text{(A-9)}$$

With this value for V_A, we can now find V_o from the series circuit consisting of R_2 and C_2 in Figure A-3.

$$V_o = \frac{V_A(1/SC_2)}{R_2 + (1/SC_2)}$$

Multiplying numerator and denominator by SC_2, we get

$$V_o = \frac{V_A}{SR_2C_2 + 1}$$

Substituting for V_A from Equation A-9 we see that

$$V_o = \frac{\dfrac{V_i\,R_1\,(SR_2C_2 + 1)SC_1}{S(R_1 + R_2)C_2 + 1 + SC_1R_1\,(SR_2C_2 + 1)}}{SR_2C_2 + 1}$$

Cancelling like terms and multiplying out the denominator gives

$$V_o = \frac{V_iSR_1C_1}{SR_1C_2 + SR_2C_2 + 1 + S^2R_1R_2C_1C_2 + SR_1C_1}$$

Rearranging in standard form,

$$V_o = \frac{V_iSR_1C_1}{S^2R_1R_2C_1C_2 + S(R_1C_1 + R_2C_2 + R_1\,C_2) + 1}$$

Divide both sides by V_i. This gives the transfer function, V_o/V_i. (Note that dividing the right-hand side by V_i simply cancels V_i from the numerator.)

$$H(S) = \frac{SR_1C_1}{S^2R_1R_2C_1C_2 + S(R_1C_1 + R_2C_2 + R_1C_2) + 1} \qquad \text{(A-10)}$$

The standard form of a comparable filter would be

$$H(S) = \frac{S\mathcal{T}_1}{(S\mathcal{T}_2 + 1)(S\mathcal{T}_3 + 1)}$$

When the denominator terms are multiplied out, this becomes

$$H(S) = \frac{S\mathcal{T}_1}{S^2\mathcal{T}_2\mathcal{T}_3 + S(\mathcal{T}_2 + \mathcal{T}_3) + 1} \qquad \text{(A-11)}$$

By comparing Equation A-10 with the standard form of a filter in Equation A-11, it is clear that the time constants, which are the coefficients of S, are given by

$$T_1 = R_1 C_1$$

$$T_2 T_3 = R_1 R_2 C_1 C_2 \qquad \text{(Call this "P")} \qquad \textbf{(A-12)}$$

$$T_2 + T_3 = R_1 C_1 + R_2 C_2 + R_1 C_2 \qquad \text{(Call this "Q")} \qquad \textbf{(A-13)}$$

Substituting the component values,

$$T_1 = 6.5 \times 10^3 \times .05 \times 10^{-6} \qquad\qquad\qquad = 3.25 \times 10^{-4}s$$

$$T_2 T_3 = 6.5 \times 10^3 \times 3.3 \times 10^3 \times .05 \times 10^{-6} \times .02 \times 10^{-6} \qquad = 2.145 \times 10^{-8}s(\text{"P"})$$

$$T_2 + T_3 = 6.5 \times 10^3 \times .05 \times 10^{-6} + 3.3 \times 10^3 \times .02 \times 10^{-6}$$
$$+ 6.5 \times 10^3 \times .02 \times 10^{-6} = 5.21 \times 10^{-4}s(\text{"Q"})$$

Using P and Q for the identity, for simplicity, and solving simultaneously for T,

$$T_2 T_3 = P$$

$$T_2 + T_3 = Q$$

$$T_2 = \frac{P}{T_3}$$

Substituting for T_2,

$$\frac{P}{T_3} + T_3 = Q$$

Multiplying by T_3,

$$P + T_3{}^2 = Q T_3$$

In standard form,

$$T_3{}^2 - Q T_3 + P = 0$$

Because this equation was derived from both the T_2 and T_3 relationships, one of the solutions gives T_2; the other gives T_3. A quadratic equation can be solved by the formula

$$x_1 \text{ and } x_2 = \frac{-b \pm \sqrt{b^2 - 4\,ac}}{2a}$$

This requires the quadratic to be in the standard form of

$$a\chi^2 + b\chi + c = 0$$

In our equation,

$$T_3{}^2 - QT_3 + P = 0$$

By comparison of forms,

$$a = 1$$
$$b = -Q$$
$$c = P$$

Therefore,

$$T_2 \text{ and } T_3 = \frac{Q \pm \sqrt{Q^2 - 4P}}{2}$$

Substituting the values of P and Q, we get

$$T_2 \text{ and } T_3 = \frac{5.21 \times 10^{-4} \pm \sqrt{(5.21 \times 10^{-4})^2 - 4 \times 2.145 \times 10^{-8}}}{2}$$

So,

$$T_2 = 4.7593 \times 10^{-4} \text{ s}$$

and

$$T_3 = 4.507 \times 10^{-5} \text{ s}$$

Recalling the value of T_1, which was found directly from R_1C_1,

$$T_1 = 3.25 \times 10^{-4} \text{ s}$$

The break frequencies can now be obtained from

$$f_1 = \frac{1}{2\pi T_1} = \frac{1}{2\pi \times 3.25 \times 10^{-4}} = 490 \text{ Hz}$$

$$f_2 = \frac{1}{2\pi T_2} = \frac{1}{2\pi \times 4.7593 \times 10^{-4}} = 334 \text{ Hz}$$

$$f_3 = \frac{1}{2\pi T_3} = \frac{1}{2\pi \times 4.507 \times 10^{-5}} = 3530 \text{ Hz}$$

Recall the equation for the standard form of this filter:

$$H(S) = \frac{S\mathcal{T}_1}{(S\mathcal{T}_2 + 1)(S\mathcal{T}_3 + 1)}$$

For calculation purposes, we can rewrite the numerator as follows:

$$S = |\omega| \text{ and } \mathcal{T}_1 = \frac{1}{\omega_1}$$

so,

$$S\mathcal{T}_1 = \frac{\omega}{\omega_1} = \frac{f}{f_1}$$

The denominator terms can be written

$$\sqrt{\left[\left(\frac{f}{f_2}\right)^2 + 1\right]\left[\left(\frac{f}{f_3}\right)^2 + 1\right]}$$

Therefore, for calculation purposes, the transfer function becomes

$$H(f) = \frac{\dfrac{f}{f_1}}{\sqrt{\left[\left(\dfrac{f}{f_2}\right)^2 + 1\right]\left[\left(\dfrac{f}{f_3}\right)^2 + 1\right]}}$$

and the level is given by

$$L_{VG} = 20 \log H(f)$$

Thus,

$$L_{VG} = 20 \log \frac{\dfrac{f}{f_1}}{\sqrt{\left[\left(\dfrac{f}{f_2}\right)^2 + 1\right]\left[\left(\dfrac{f}{f_3}\right)^2 + 1\right]}}$$

Entering the actual break frequencies, we get

$$L_{VG} = 20 \log \frac{\dfrac{f}{490}}{\sqrt{\left[\left(\dfrac{f}{334}\right)^2 + 1\right]\left[\left(\dfrac{f}{3530}\right)^2 + 1\right]}} \qquad \text{(A-14)}$$

We can now construct the Bode plot. We can also draw the calculated response curve from Equation A-14. For these graphs, it is best to use semi-logarithmic paper, in which the horizontal axis is incremented in powers of 10, or in octaves (base 2). Either gives a constant horizontal increment per octave. To draw the Bode plot, start by drawing vertical dotted lines at each break frequency. Because the transfer function is

$$H(S) = \frac{S\mathcal{T}_1}{(S\mathcal{T}_2 + 1)(S\mathcal{T}_3 + 1)}$$

the numerator, $S\mathcal{T}_1$, causes an upward sloping line of 6 dB/octave (see Figure A-5). This line strikes the 0 dB level when the value of $S\mathcal{T}_1$ equals 1. A gain of 1 corresponds to 0 dB, so the Bode construction can start with a +6 dB/octave slope, starting at the lowest level and reaching the 0 dB level at frequency f_1. (In order to draw a 6 dB/octave slope on base 10 logarithmic paper, it might be useful to realize that 6 dB/octave forms a slope of 20 dB/decade. *Decade* equals ten times the frequency.)

Fig. A-5
Bandpass filter response

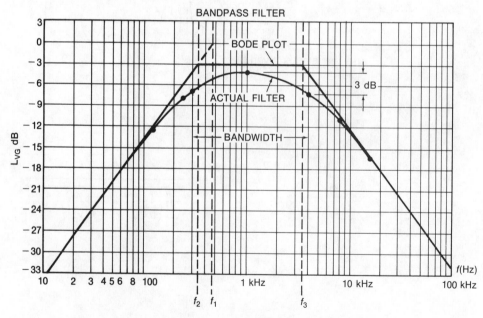

The two terms $(S\mathcal{T}_2+1)$ and $(S\mathcal{T}_3+1)$ are both *poles*, being denominator terms. Therefore, at break frequencies f_2 and f_3, the slope is reduced by 6 dB/octave. Because the original slope was +6 dB/octave at break frequency f_2, draw a horizontal line starting from the upward sloping line at the point where it cuts frequency f_2. (This appears to be at about −3 dB.)

The next pole turns the Bode down to a −6 dB/octave slope at frequency f_3. Notice that the Bode never quite reaches the 0 dB level. The horizontal part of the plot is at about −3 dB.

In order to plot the filtering effect, plot the calculated level gain at each octave, starting from 15.625 Hz. An HP 11 program for this calculation is shown in the box on page 238, along with the response in Table A-2. For the first run only, initialize with keystrokes **g RTN, 15.625, STO 0**. Then key **f B**. The frequency will be displayed. To find the output level at this frequency, press **R/S**. It is only necessary to key **f B** and **R/S** for each subsequent reading. The frequencies will be incremented in octaves automatically. To repeat the entire sequence, key in **15.625, STO 0**, then **f B** and **R/S**.

Table A-2 Level gain response

Frequency (Hz)	L_{VG} dB
15.625	− 29.9
31.25	− 23.9
62.5	− 18
125	− 12.4
250	− 7.8
500	− 5
1,000	− 4.1
2,000	− 4.7
4,000	− 6.9
8,000	− 11.2
16,000	− 16.7

Transfer Function of LF Equivalent Circuits

(See *Bandpass Characteristic* in Chapter 6.)

From the LF equivalent transformer circuit in Figure 6-11A, the transfer function is defined as

$$H(S) = \frac{V_L}{V_i} = \frac{Z_L}{Z_i} \quad \text{(by the Voltage Proportionality Law).}$$

Program for Calculating Level Gain

Program	Initialization	
f Lbl B	g RTN	
RCL 0	15.625	First run only
R/S	STO 0	
334	f B	
÷	R/S	
gx^2		
1		
+		
RCL 0		
3530		
÷		
gx^2		
1		
+		
x		
$\sqrt{x}$		
$1/x$		
RCL 0		
490		
÷		
x		
g log		
20		
x		
STO 1		
RCL 0		
2		
x		
STO 0		
RCL 1		
g RTN		

But,

$$Z_L = \frac{SL_M R_L}{SL_M + R_L} \quad (L_M \text{ and } R_L \text{ being in parallel}).$$

And,

$$Z_i = R_o + \frac{SL_M R_L}{SL_M + R_L}$$

Using a common denominator,

$$Z_i = \frac{SL_M R_o + R_o R_L + SL_M R_L}{SL_M + R_L}$$

But,

$$H(S) = \frac{Z_L}{Z_i} = \frac{\dfrac{SL_M R_L}{SL_M + R_L}}{\dfrac{SL_M R_o + SL_M R_L + R_o R_L}{SL_M + R_L}}$$

The two fractional denominators $(SL_M + R_L)$ cancel; therefore,

$$H(S) = \frac{SL_M R_L}{SL_M(R_o + R_L) + R_o R_L}$$

Divide out k, the DC gain, which occurs when reactance is zero, and,

$$K = \frac{R_L}{R_o + R_L}$$

Then,

$$H(S) = \frac{R_L}{R_o + R_L}\left(\frac{SL_M}{SL_M + \dfrac{R_o R_L}{R_o + R_L}}\right)$$

Multiply the numerator and denominator by $\dfrac{R_o + R_L}{R_o R_L}$, to obtain the standard form, which was given in Chapter 6.

$$H(S) = \frac{R_L}{R_o + R_L}\left(\frac{SL_M\left[\dfrac{R_o + R_L}{R_o R_L}\right]}{SL_M\left[\dfrac{R_o + R_L}{R_o R_L}\right] + 1}\right)$$

Hysteresis

(See *Bandpass Characteristic* in Chapter 6 and *Mechanical and Electrical Requirements* in Chapter 8.)

Hysteresis is a scientific term that describes a certain type of energy loss that occurs when an action is initiated or reversed. It is due to a kind of friction.

To illustrate this, consider an extreme case in which a rusty old spring has to be compressed and then released a number of times. A certain amount of compression force has to be applied before the spring even starts to move. This is due to friction. From then on, the spring compression increases in proportion to the increasing force.

When it is time for the spring to be allowed to expand to its original state, it is found that as the force starts to be reduced, the spring does not immediately respond. It remains stationary due to friction. When the force is reduced enough, however, the spring starts to expand, and this expansion continues in proportion to the reduction of the applied force.

At each reversal of the applied force, there is a lag due to friction, before the movement of the spring responds. This is a typical hysteresis phenomenon. The distance moved, d, as the spring is compressed could be plotted vertically against the applied force, F, plotted horizontally. This is shown in Figure A-6A. Notice that a loop is formed. This is called a *hysteresis loop*. The area within the loop gives a measure of the loss of energy that occurs at each cycle of compression and expansion.

A similar phenomenon occurs when a magnetizing force from a magnetic field, H, is applied to a piece of permeable material, such as iron. There is a similar lag in the strength of magnetization, B, which has been induced in the iron. Similarly, at each reversal of magnetizing force, there is a lag in the magnetic response of the iron. This is due to the friction that the domains experience inside the iron as they try to reverse their orientation.

A graph is shown in Figure A-6B of induced magnetization in the iron, B, plotted vertically against the magnetizing force, H, plotted horizontally.

Fig. A-6
Hysteresis loops

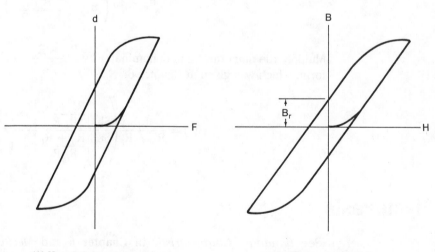

(A) Hysteresis in a rusty spring   *(B) Hysteresis of soft iron*

The amount of **magnetization remaining** in the material after the magnetizing force has been withdrawn (has reduced to zero) is indicated by the height, B_r. This is called the *retentivity* of the magnetic material.

The slope of the straight portion of the graph represents the ease with which the material can be magnetized by the magnetic field. This is called its *permeability*. It is the rate of increase of magnetization (magnetic flux) with respect to an increase of magnetizing force (field strength). The permeability is often designated by the Greek letter μ. Thus, $\mu = dB/dH$.

In cgs (centimeter, gram, second) units, the permeability of air or a vacuum is taken as unity. If the material is soft iron, the permeability is much greater, because iron has the ability to concentrate a magnetic field into a small area. The relative permeability of iron to air is about 600 to 1.

Note that the flux density is the intensity of magnetization within the material. The magnetic field strength is the magnetizing force that is producing flux in the material. This is often specified in *ampere turns per meter*, because an electromagnet produces a field that is proportional to the current and the number of turns, distributed along its length, which is measured in meters. Permeability is the ease with which a material can be magnetized. Retentivity is the amount of flux remaining after a material has been fully magnetized and the magnetizing force has been removed.

Glossary

Glossary

Active Component A semiconductor or vacuum tube. Any electronic component whose action is altered in response to an applied voltage other than the input, or whose action depends on input polarity.

Alias False. In digital systems, an invalid audible frequency created by the interaction of the sampling frequency with the true audio frequency.

Amplitude The height of the peak value of a wave above the zero reference value.

Analog A continuously variable waveform. A smooth curve, forming a continuum of values between any two points.

Analog-to-Digital Converter A device that converts a series of sample voltages to their corresponding numerical binary values.

Asymptote A straight line to which a curve approaches ever more closely, but never quite reaches.

Audio Signal A fluctuating voltage, whose value fluctuates in proportion to the instantaneous pressure of a sound wave.

Azimuth In general, a vertical line from the zenith to the horizon. In magnetic tape, a line perpendicular to the tape edge, thus forming a right angle with the edge of the tape.

Balanced Line A line that carries a signal or voltage on two conductors in which the voltage is equally balanced on either side of ground potential. If the voltage is AC, the two line voltages are always 180° out of phase with each other. In other words, they are always of equal and opposite polarity.

Bandwidth The extent of the range of frequencies within certain limits. Frequencies at which the signal has fallen by more than 3 dB from its maximum are said to have been cut off. These are called the cutoff frequencies, and they form the limits of the band. The bandwidth is the frequency difference between the high cutoff frequency and the low cutoff frequency.

Bar A measure of air pressure. One bar equals 10^5 pascals. One pascal is 1 newton per square meter. The value of 10^5 is chosen because it is a convenient approximation to standard atmospheric pressure, which is 1.03×10^5 pascals.

Bel The exponent of the ratio of a value to a reference value. In bel units, the value is specified as a level. Thus, a power level is the log (exponent) of P/P_{ref}, where P is the power in watts and P_{ref} is a reference power, usually taken as 1 mW. Similarly, a voltage level is the log of V/V_{ref}, where V is the voltage and V_{ref} is the reference voltage, usually 0.775 V. In audio technology, levels are evaluated in decibels, rather than in bels. A decibel is one-tenth of a bel.

Binary A type of number system, based on 2. In a binary system, each more significant column is twice the value of the previous column. This means that a binary number contains only two digits, 0 and 1. The value 2 is interpreted as a 1 carried into the next more significant column.

Bode Plot A graph of output level in dBs, plotted on a frequency base scaled in octaves (that is, logarithmically). The graph is made up entirely of straight lines. Each line represents the resistive or reactive effect of one or more filtering elements. Each angle, where the lines *break* into different slopes, occurs at a *break frequency*.

Break Frequency The frequency at which a reactive filtering effect of ±6 dB/octave, starting from zero frequency, strikes the Bode plot. At this frequency, the new reactive effect causes a *break* in the direction of the Bode plot, either increasing or reducing its slope by ±6 dB/octave. The break frequency is sometimes called the *corner frequency* or *knee*.

Capacitance The ability of a capacitor to store an electrical charge.

Capacitor A component that can store electrical energy in the form of an electrical charge.

Charge The electrical state of a particle. An excess of electrons creates a negative charge. A reduction of electrons (sometimes called an excess of *holes*) creates a positive charge. The unit of charge, the coulomb, consists of 6.25×10^{18} electrons.

Complex Frequency Variable An AC frequency in complex number form. A complex number contains a number term (the resistive effect of a filter, at

zero phase angle) and a *j* term (the reactive effect, at 90° phase angle). However, resistance is frequency independent; therefore, in filter analysis, the number term is zero. Consequently, the complex frequency variable, designated by the letter S, contains only a *j* term. It is given by $S = j\omega$, where ω is the radial frequency—that is, the frequency measured in radians/second. One cycle (360°) equals 2π radians, so $j\omega = j2\pi f$, where f is the cyclical frequency, measured in cycles/second.

Compressor A component that reduces the dynamic range of an audio signal. This is achieved by a voltage controlled amplifier that reduces the gain of high-level signals.

Constant Voltage Coupling A coupling between two stages, in which the voltage reaching the second stage is at least 90 percent of the open circuit voltage of the first stage.

Corner Frequency See *Break Frequency*.

Current The rate of flow of electrons. As electrons flow in one direction, the spaces left behind, called *holes*, appear to flow in the opposite direction. Thus, current can be visualized as electron flow (negative current flow) or, in the opposite direction, *holes* flow (positive current flow, sometimes called conventional current flow).

Cutoff Frequency The frequency at which the signal falls off by 3 dB from its maximum value.

Darlington Pair Two transistors connected as emitter followers, so that the current gain of the first is amplified by the current gain of the second. Often used as a high-gain audio amplifier output stage.

Decibel One-tenth of a bel. See *Bel*.

Digital A type of system in which the processing is done by digital logic. Digital logic recognizes only two values, called 1 and 0, high and low, or true and false. There can be no continuous variation of values in digital systems. All value changes must occur in discrete steps, the minimum step being of unit size.

Digital-to-Analog Converter A device that converts instantaneous binary values to their corresponding voltages.

Domain The smallest known magnetic field within a magnetized material. A domain is presumed to act as a small bar magnet with a north pole at one end and a south pole at the other. In the Domain Theory of Magnetism, a solid permeable material is assumed to contain multitudes of domains.

Doping The process of diffusing a small quantity of non-semiconductor material into the pure material of which semiconductors are made. Doping material is of two kinds: trivalent doping contains three valent electrons, and pentavalent doping contains five valent electrons.

Dynamic Range The ratio of the greatest to least sound intensity, or greatest to least signal voltage.

Equalizer A component that can boost or cut the signal level at a predetermined frequency. A shelving equalizer can supply boost/cut at the high or low frequencies, its level of gain flattening out at the frequency extremes. A parametric equalizer can boost or cut the signal at any selected frequency within the audible range.

Expander A component that expands the dynamic range. This is achieved by a voltage controlled amplifier that reduces the gain of low-level signals.

FET Field effect transistor. A unipolar semiconductor through which the current flow is controlled by an electrostatic field

Filter A device for changing the frequency response of a signal, so that its output level becomes frequency dependent. Its gain (or loss) will then be different at different frequencies.

Gain The ratio of output voltage (or power) to input voltage (or power).

Ground Zero reference point of voltage. Called *ground* because the capacitance

of actual ground (the earth) is so huge that no amount of current flow into or out of it will measurably change its voltage.

Harmonics Whole number multiples of the fundamental frequency. Twice the fundamental is the second harmonic, three times the fundamental is the third harmonic, etc.

Henry The unit of inductance.

Hertz A unit of frequency. One hertz equals one cycle/second.

Holes See *Current*.

Hysteresis Loss of energy due to an alternating physical activity, such as magnetizing and demagnetizing an iron core (see Appendix A).

IC Integrated circuit. A miniaturized active circuit constructed on a single semiconductor chip.

Impedance The total opposition to current flow resulting from the combined effects of resistance and reactance.

Inductance The ability of a coil, whenever it conducts current, to extract electrical energy and store this in the form of a magnetic field.

Inductor A coil.

Ion An electrically charged atom.

Kirchoff's Current Law The total current entering any point in a circuit equals the total current leaving that point.

Kirchoff's Voltage Law In a series circuit, the sum of the voltage rises equals the sum of the voltage drops.

Level The magnitude of a physical quantity in bel or dB units.

Level Gain The difference in level between two points.

Load That part of a circuit in which useful work is done; the component that the circuit was designed to energize.

Logarithm The exponent of a power to a given base.

Microphone A transducer that converts acoustical energy into electrical energy.

Mixer An audio component in which signals from various channels can be mixed. Each channel input incorporates a fader, which determines what proportion of the channel signal is incorporated in the final output (or mixdown).

MOSFET Metal-oxide semiconductor field effect transistor. This is a field effect transistor in which the gate is insulated from the channel by a thin layer of metal-oxide insulating material. It has certain advantages over the junction FET (J-FET).

Newton A unit of force in the MKS (Meter, Kilogram, Second) system of units.

Noise A random fluctuating mix of all audible frequencies. Low-level noise forms a natural background to all audible sounds.

Ohm's Law Current flow is proportional to the voltage, and inversely proportional to the resistance.

Open Circuit A circuit in which the output terminals are open—that is, with no load connected.

Operational Amplifier (Op-Amp) A high-quality, low-power differential amplifier, suitable for line-level signal voltages, usually manufactured as an integrated circuit. Its characteristics are high gain, high input impedance, and low output impedance.

Pascal A unit of pressure, defined as 1 newton per square meter.

Passive Filter A filter made up of passive components, which cannot amplify. Its effect is obtained by selectively attenuating certain frequencies.

PCB Printed circuit board.

Pole A single filtering element, which causes an attenuation of signal level, as frequency rises, at a rate of 6 dB/octave. The break frequency at which such an effect starts is often called a *pole* of the function.

Post-emphasis Equalization applied to a signal immediately after being reproduced by a magnetic replay head.

Pre-amplifier A component designed to amplify very small signal voltages, such as those from a microphone or tape head.

Pre-emphasis Equalization applied to a signal immediately prior to recording by a magnetic record head.

Power Amplifier The final stage of amplification in an audio chain. Its function is to increase the power of the processed signal, so that it can drive the loudspeakers sufficiently hard to produce the required sound volume.

Quiescent Voltage The DC voltage at any point in a circuit, when power is switched on but no signal is passing.

Radial Frequency The frequency of an AC signal measured in radians/second, as opposed to cycles/second. One cycle equals 2π radians.

Reactance Opposition to current flow due to the reaction of a capacitor or inductor to the AC frequency.

Rectifier A component, such as a diode, that passes current only in one direction and can, therefore, be used to convert AC to DC.

Semiconductor Material made up of atoms having an outer sphere containing four valent electrons. Such material can be used to construct an active electronic component comprising two or more differently doped wafers of semiconductor material. Examples include diodes, transistors, and integrated circuits.

Shelving Equalizer See *Equalizer*.

Signal A series of voltage (or current) fluctuations that parallels the fluctuating air pressure as sound waves pass a given point.

Transducer A component that converts acoustical, mechanical, or magnetic energy into electrical energy, or vice versa.

Transfer Function The ratio of a filter's output voltage to input voltage. It is necessarily a function of frequency, because the purpose of a filter is to produce an output that is frequency dependent.

Transistor See *Semiconductor*.

VTVM Vacuum tube voltmeter. It has an extremely high input impedance and can be used to obtain accurate voltage readings, even of very low voltages in highly resistive circuits.

Watt The unit of electrical power, equal to one joule of work per second. It can be evaluated from the product of voltage times current.

Zero A single filtering element, which causes an increase in signal level of 6 dB/octave as frequency rises. The break frequency at which such an effect starts is often called a *zero* of the function.

Index

How to Build Speaker Enclosures
Badmaieff and Davis

A practical guide to the whys and hows of constructing high quality, top performance speaker enclosures. A wooden box alone is not a speaker enclosure—size, baffling, sound insulation, speaker characteristics, and crossover points must all be carefully considered.

The book contains many detailed drawings and instructions for building the various basic types of enclosures, including the infinite-baffle, the bass-reflex, and the horn-projector types, as well as different combinations of these.

This practical book covers both the advantages and disadvantages of each enclosure type and includes a discussion of speaker drivers, crossover networks, and hints on the techniques of construction and testing.

Topics covered include:
- Speaker Enclosures
- Drivers for Enclosures
- Infinite Baffles
- Bass-Reflex or Phase-Inversion Enclosures
- Horn Enclosures
- Combination Enclosures
- Crossover Networks
- Construction and Testing Techniques

144 Pages, 5½ x 8½, Softbound
ISBN: 0-672-20520-3
No. 20520, $6.95

Introduction to Professional Recording Techniques
Bruce Bartlett

This all-inclusive introduction to the equipment and techniques for state-of-the-art recording—whether in residences or professional studios or on location—offers a wealth of valuable information on topics not found in other books on audio recording.

Geared primarily for the audio hobbyist or aspiring professional, this book delivers a comprehensive discussion of recording engineering and production techniques, including special coverage of microphones and microphone techniques, sampling, sequencing, and MIDI. It provides up-to-date coverage of monitoring, special effects, hum prevention, and spoken-word recording, as well as special sections on recognizing good sound and troubleshooting bad sound.

Topics covered include:
- The Recording and Reproduction Chain
- Simple Home Recording
- Setting Up the Studio
- Microphones and Microphone Techniques
- Control-Room Techniques
- On-Location Recording
- Judging the Recording
- Appendices: dB or not dB, Introduction to SMPTE Time Code, and Further Education

416 Pages, 7½ x 9¾, Softbound
ISBN: 0-672-22574-3
No. 22574, $24.95

John D. Lenk's Troubleshooting & Repair of Audio Equipment
John D. Lenk

This manual provides the most up-to-date data available and a simplified approach to practical troubleshooting and repair of major audio devices. It will enable both the beginning and the intermediate level technician or hobbyist to apply tips and tricks to any specific equipment.

This book also includes such time-saving hints as circuit-by-circuit troubleshooting based on failure or trouble symptoms, universal step-by-step procedures, and actual procedures recommended by manufacturers' service personnel.

Topics covered include:
- Introduction to Modern Audio Equipment Troubleshooting
- Troubleshooting and Repair of Amplifiers and Loudspeakers
- Troubleshooting and Repair of Linear-Tracking Turntables
- Troubleshooting and Repair of Audio Cassette Decks
- Troubleshooting and Repair of AM/FM Stereo Tuners
- Troubleshooting and Repair of CD Players

208 Pages, 8½ x 11, Softbound
ISBN: 0-672-22517-4
No. 22517, $21.95

Modern Recording Techniques, Third Edition
David Miles Huber and Robert A. Runstein

Recording engineers, technicians, and audio engineering students will appreciate this updated version of the best-selling *Modern Recording Techniques*. It has been completely updated with new information on state-of-the-art audio topics including digital audio, random access audio, and the use of digital technologies in audio production.

The book provides a basis for intelligence and understanding of recording technology, allowing the reader to get a feel for the entire scope of procedures. The book's comprehensive coverage makes it an ideal reference for the practicing or aspiring recording engineer.

Topics covered include:
- Introduction
- Sound and Hearing
- Studio Acoustics
- Microphones: Design and Technique
- The Analog Audio Tape Recorder
- Digital Technology
- MIDI and Electronic Musical Instrument Technology
- Synchronization
- The Amplifier
- The Audio Production Console
- Signal Processors
- Noise Reduction Devices
- Monitor Speakers
- Product Manufacture
- Studio Session Procedures
- Tomorrow's Industry: Just Around the Corner

400 Pages, 7½ x 9¾, Softbound
ISBN: 0-672-22682-0
No. 22682, $26.95

Visit your local book retailer or call
800-428-SAMS.

Musical Applications of Microprocessors
Second Edition
Hal Chamberlin

This expanded and revised edition covers analog, digital, and microprocessor sound and music synthesis. Its nonmathematical language makes the material accessible to musicians and computer users, as well as engineers.

New synthesis techniques, nonlinear waveshaping, Vosim, and the Fourier transform are covered and supported with program listings in BASIC and 68000 assembly language.

An entirely new section examines the practical application of synthesis theory in actual synthesis products, including professional and studio equipment, novelty products using modern synthesis techniques, and sound generation circuits.

Topics covered include:
- Music Synthesis Principles
- Sound Modification Methods
- Direct Computer Synthesis Methods
- Computer-Controlled Analog Synthesis
- Digital-to-Analog and Analog-to-Digital Converters
- Control Sequence Display and Editing
- Digital Synthesis and Sound Modification
- Source-Signal Analysis
- Product Applications and the Future

816 Pages, 6¼ x 9¼, Hardbound
ISBN: 0-672-45768-7
No. 45768, $39.95

Sound System Engineering, Second Edition
Don and Carolyn Davis

Like the first edition, this comprehensive text will provide you with useful information for the day-to-day work of designing sound systems—with much more material and in-depth coverage of subjects. It is a practical manual that carefully examines methods of accurately predicting such variables as acoustic gain, clarity of sound, and required electrical input power while plans are still on the drawing board.

Topics covered include:
- Audio Systems
- Mathematics for Audio Systems
- Using the Decibel
- Impedance Matching
- Interfacing Electrical and Acoustics Systems
- Loudspeaker Directivity and Coverage
- The Acoustic Environment
- Large-Room Acoustics
- Small-Room Acoustics
- Designing for Speech Intelligibility
- Designing for Acoustic Gain
- Microphones
- Loudspeakers and Loudspeaker Arrays
- Using Delay Devices
- Installing the Sound System
- Equalizing the Sound System
- Audio and Acoustic Instrumentation
- Putting it All Together
- Specifications

688 Pages, 7½ x 9¾, Hardbound
ISBN: 0-672-21857-7
No. 21857, $49.95

The Microphone Manual: Design and Application
David Miles Huber

This excellent reference bridges the gap between the equipment manufacturer and the microphone user by clearly introducing and explaining microphone design, characteristics, and theory. The book is written for intermediate to advanced audio users, professional audio and video technicians and engineers, and students. The latest microphone technology—including wireless microphones, clip and boundary microphones, electrical characteristics of the microphone, single and stereo microphone placement techniques—is fully detailed and illustrated.

Topics covered include:
- Basic Theory of Operation
- The Microphone Transducer
- Microphone Characteristics
- Electrical Interface-Cable/ Connector
- Microphone Accessories
- Fundamentals of Single-Microphone Techniques
- Fundamentals of Stereo-Microphone Techniques
- Applied Microphone Techniques in Music Production
- Applied Microphone Techniques in Video/Film Production
- Speech and Music Reinforcement
- Appendices: The Use of Omnidirectional Microphones for Modern Recording, Microphone Techniques for Predictable Tonal Balance Control, the PZM™ Boundary Booklet, Listing of Popular Professional Microphones, Glossary

336 Pages, 7½ x 9¾, Softbound
ISBN: 0-672-22598-0
No. 22598, $29.95

Principles of Digital Audio
Second Edition
Ken C. Pohlmann

Beginning with the fundamentals of numbers, sampling, and quantizing, this is a comprehensive look at digital audio, complete with the latest technologies such as CD-I, CD-V, and DAT.

This second edition of a popular text serves equally well as a technical reference, a user's handbook, or a textbook and is written by one of the country's leading audio experts. It includes new information on digital signal processing, CD technology, and magnetic storage, as it seeks to provide an in-depth understanding of this ever-changing technology.

Topics covered include:
- Audio and Digital Basics
- Fundamentals of Digital Audio
- Digital Audio Recording and Reproduction
- Alternative Digitization Methods
- Coding, Interfacing, and Transmission
- Error Correction
- Magnetic Storage
- Digital Audio Tape (DAT)
- Optical Storage and Transmission
- The Compact Disc
- Digital Signal Processing
- Digital Audio Workstations

474 Pages, 7½ x 9¾, Softbound
ISBN: 0-672-22634-0
No. 22634, $29.95

Visit your local book retailer or call
800-428-SAMS.